And now these three remain:
faith, hope and love.

These Three

By Tom Pfingsten

Inspired by true events

Art by Alex Boren

THESE THREE
A Bring Me Hope publication
First Edition

2169 Green Canyon Road
Fallbrook, California 92028

www. bringmehope. org
(760) 723 – 5885

Printed in China

POEM OF CONTENTS

This is how [a damaged boy]

Each time a new criminal is escorted into Commissioner Chen's office on the third floor of his police department, the tall, serious chief has a routine. First, he cuffs the suspect to a heavy wooden chair by the door. Then he unpins his badge and sets it just out of sight—behind a stack of reports or in an open drawer. Next he removes his handgun and places it somewhere prominent on the desk, muzzle pointing in the general direction of the perpetrator. Elbows on desktop, arms tilted up into a perfect triangle and, beneath his chin, hands clasped: This is how he sizes up a culprit.

But this one. This one has already received uncharacteristic leniency, including the free use of his little hands. Both gun and badge are out of sight. The commissioner is no stranger to criminals-in-training—at least that's what the deputies call them here in the eastern Chinese province of Anhui. Shoplifters. Worse. *It's sad how corrupt some of this city's youngsters are becoming,* he thinks. *But this one—there's something different about him* Across the desk a scrawny boy does his best to fill the old wooden chair that's held murderers and grieving mothers in turn. The handcuff marks on his wrists are fading as he struggles to get comfortable, trying somehow to make his arms seem at ease on the armrests, which are up around his shoulders. His feet swing five inches off the ground and he seems strangely content—cheerful even. He compliments Supervisor Chen on his wooden chair, praising its sturdiness. He looks around the office like he's sizing it up for new curtains. He does not seem at all concerned that he's just been arrested, nor that a senior officer is considering him in cold silence.

Finally Chen leans back and squints.

"Okay, boy. How old are you?"

"Eight," says the boy.

"Eight?" the commissioner replies, eyebrows rising. "You're a small eight. What's your name?"

"Junjie," he chirps.

Outside the office is a clear view of downtown, where thousands of people are walking to work, haggling with street vendors and enjoying a brief interlude of winter sunshine.

"Well, Junjie," says the officer, "it's time for you to explain why you were shoplifting this morning."

A flash of unease crosses the boy's face, but no remorse. He fingers a series of notches carved into the chair by a previous lawbreaker.

"Look," Chen continues, "if it was just a couple pears, I'm not going to lock you up. But unless you start talking, I will be forced to treat you like any other criminal."

Nothing.

"All right, let's get you booked," says the commissioner, reaching for his telephone.

"Where do I start?" the boy interjects quietly, as if to himself.

The officer loosens his tie and reclines.

"The beginning," he says.

Well, first there were the frozen toes, and my nose was throbbing from the cold howling wind that came in from the mountains yesterday to sting any part of me that did not fit into this ratty jacket and sorry shoes that have been too small since last summer.

Smokes and liquor, my father's two true loves—them and thievery are what keep him alive. Me? I just try to stay warm in the winter and out of trouble the rest of the time.

I'm in trouble now, I know. I know.

But as I was saying: Yesterday. Smokes. Father left me there on the sidewalk—my usual spot—and went inside to buy a pack. I started counting city busses. They run every ten minutes—twelve when it snows—and I had counted at least four when I started to wonder. Usually I see just one and then we're on our way. But four. I knew something had to be wrong.

I ran up the steps and inside and I remember thinking, so that's what the shopkeeper looks like. Shorter than I imagined. I asked him where my father was and he just started yelling.

"How old are you?" he said.

I told him ten and he called me a liar.

"You're no more than six," he shouted. "And even if you were ten, you couldn't be in here. I sell liquor and tobacco. You go!"

But I was not leaving until I found that no-good father of mine, and I told him that. Even with the dim light from a single bulb, I could see that he wasn't in the front of the shop. The owner jabbed his cigarette toward the door to an unlit stock room.

"That's the only other room in this place," he said. "Maybe he went in there."

I stepped quickly toward the back of the store, calling

for him.

"Father?" I said. "Are you in here?"

I saw a string and pulled it. Nothing happened for a moment—then a flicker. The room lit up and father wasn't there. I heard footsteps behind me and turned right into the handle of a broom. It hit my jaw—smack! —and I saw the storekeeper smirk before my head hit a shelf and I blacked out.

I woke up with a sore neck in the back of a strange car. I laid still for a few minutes, trying to recall what had happened. I raised my head enough to see the shopkeeper's face in the rear view mirror, suddenly remembering his sinister face and the crack of the broom handle.

"Where are you taking me?" I asked him. I sat up, angry and scared. I didn't want to let the scared show.

He smiled and grunted. "You think this is the first time I've busted a punk shoplifter?"

I told him it wasn't the first time I'd been busted. I said, "This is illegal, even if I had been shoplifting, which I wasn't. You're just a no-good cashier, you have no right to hit me, take me hostage."

He said I wasn't hostage, said if he'd called the police I would be in the back seat of a car with a sore head anyways. He told me to shut up.

We must have been miles away from the store because

I didn't recognize any of the buildings outside the fogged-up windows. It was dusk, and snowing. It had gotten colder. I asked him if he was taking me to the police station.

"You wish." That was the last thing he said, and he was right.

Five minutes later, we turned off the boulevard into an alley and rolled to a stop behind another car, only this one was sleek and black—the kind I've only seen on TV. They drive them in Beijing, Shanghai. Not here.

The shopkeeper killed the engine and honked twice, and three men in expensive clothes got out of the other car. Two of them were tall and muscular, the third was short and thin, like a blade of grass. He had long hair and rings on most of his fingers, and his eyes were blank, like they were saying, *Whatever it is, I don't care.* He scared me like stray dogs scare me.

When the three men were standing in a line behind their car, facing ours, the shopkeeper seemed spooked— maybe more than me—and after a few seconds, he told me to get out. I shook my head.

"You will exit the car here," he said, turning his head to look at me. I buckled my seat belt. He looked again at the man with the ponytail, who held out a hand, like this, like he was in a hurry. The shopkeeper turned back to me, and I could see panic and anger on his face. He started to say something, then yanked his door open and jumped out into the alley, moving toward the rear door.

I hit the lock, wishing I had already tried to run. The keys were still in the ignition, so I locked the driver's door, as well, sealing myself off from the men in the alley. One of the tall men walked down the right side of the car, crossing his hands in front of him while the shopkeeper kicked the door on my left and cursed. The boss from the black car said something; he didn't sound impressed.

"No, I've got it," said the liquor store man. He took off his jacket and wrapped it around his fist. When he looked at me again through the window, he looked different. "I've got him" —that's what he said.

Then—I couldn't believe it—he punched the glass. It didn't break the first time so he pulled back for a second hit. My heart was already beating hard in my chest, but until then, I hadn't panicked. I had been through worse. As the shopkeeper's fist thudded against the glass a second time, I knew I was in serious trouble. Through the windshield, I could see the boss man blowing into his hands. Steam from the fancy car's tailpipe filled the alley. The gray dusk grew darker, swirls of snow descended. And I prayed. Mother told me I could if I ever got in trouble.

The shopkeeper's third punch cracked the window in several directions. I looked over just as his arm was swinging for the last time. Little cubes of glass exploded into the car, peppering my face and scattering across the vinyl seat. He stuck both arms through the window, in one motion unbuck-ling my seat belt and grabbing a handful of my hair. I tried to resist, tried to hold onto the seat in front of me, but he was too strong. He yanked once and I tumbled into the street. My stomach scraped against the broken glass left on the window frame and I noticed several cuts on his arms, as well. I prepared for a beating.

Instead, the next thing I felt was a warm hand on my neck. Then one on my arm. I peeked over my shoulder to see the man with the ponytail crouching behind me.

"You're hurt, child," he said, "but we'll fix you up. Let me see your belly." I rolled over and he pulled up my bloody shirt, then snapped his fingers behind him. One of his men brought a first-aid kit, and he spent the next five minutes cleaning and bandaging my skin. I was surprised by how gentle he was—like a real doctor. He even smiled and made small talk while he was cleaning the cuts, but his eyes were still empty and cold.

When he was done, I sat up and the shopkeeper looked like he would have beaten me to death there in the alley if not for the three strangers. His hands were shiny red from trying to stop the bleeding on his forearms. He stepped for-ward and reached for the first-aid kit, but the boss man yanked it away.

I remember exactly what he said, because it was the first time he raised his voice. "That's for our clients," he said, "not for half-witted shopkeepers who hurt themselves because of their stupidity." Then he stood up and snapped again, wiping my blood off his hands. A sidekick took the first-aid kit and handed him a roll of bills, hundred-Yuan notes bundled tightly with a rubber band. Then he looked at my kidnapper, who was becoming more anxious by the minute. Tapping the roll of money on his leg, the man looked like he was making a decision.

"Look," said the shopkeeper, "just pay me and I'll go." He held his arms out in front of him; blood was dripping onto the snow. "Look what I've been through today."

The other man scoffed, said he didn't deserve the money. He said, "You deliver me a damaged boy and expect full payment?"

The liquor store man started to say something about me, about being spirited and how that was worth extra, but the boss slapped him and he fell against the brick wall.

"I need unharmed boys!" he shouted. "Unharmed!" He smoothed his coat and his jet-black hair. The shopkeeper was holding his face, and I could see anger returning where a minute ago there was just fear. He bent over like he was going to collapse, inhaled, and then lunged at the ponytailed man. But one of the sidekicks took a fast step forward and punched the shopkeeper in the side of the head with a gloved fist. I admit I did like to see him get handled like that, put down in the snow.

The boss insulted him again, then motioned both of us toward the idling vehicle. I knew I couldn't mess with this guy, so I went. Before all the doors were even shut, the driver hit the gas and we flew out the other end of the alley. I was wedged between the bleeding shopkeeper and one of the hired men in the backseat, but I could see out the front as we weaved at top speed through empty streets and narrow corridors that were obviously familiar to the driver.

After ten minutes, I noticed that the buildings had changed. Instead of storefronts peddling vacuum cleaners and cheap clothes, there were empty industrial hangars on both sides. The driver slowed, slipped between two of the buildings, and honked at the brick wall in front of us. It began to rise, and light flooded out into the street.

Inside was a wide, tall room with several other sleek vehicles and weapons on the walls. When the wall had risen just high enough, we pulled in and I noticed a man flip a switch by a doorway on the far side of the room, lowering it again behind us.

I was the last to exit the car, and when I did someone

shoved a cloth bag over my head, fastening both my hands behind me with a plastic tie wrap. I didn't dare struggle. I still wasn't sure what these men wanted with me, but it was not the time to make trouble for myself. When I was prodded, I walked, and the men guided me through several doorways and up a flight of stairs. At one point I knew we had gone outside because of the temperature—freezing, like the night air back in the alley. After a few minutes, we stopped walking, and the bag was removed.

This new room didn't have a single bed or sofa—only three computer workstations and a row of telephones on the wall. It was well-lit and warm, but oddly disturbing. Just standing there, looking around, I thought I was going to pass out. I've been in some tight spots before, had some close calls, but I've never felt anything like what I felt in that room.

I was told to sit, so I sat, sliding to the floor next to a doorway that led into another room with a refrigerator and a sink. As the two sidekicks sat down at their workstations, the boss shouted toward the kitchen.

"We're thirsty, girl," he yelled.

In a moment, a girl about my age came around the corner with a tray of beverages. She glanced at me as she walked by, and the look in her eyes sent shivers down my spine. It wasn't fear or anger or pain written on her face—

it was hopelessness, a blank and distanced stare. She served the men, then tucked the tray under her arm and started back-pedaling toward the kitchen.

"And something for our guest," the boss told her, nodding toward me. She hurried back a few seconds later with a juice box, holding the straw to my lips. I started to whisper a question, but she shoved the straw in my mouth and squeezed the box. She was watching the men closely, never changing her expression.

She was terrifying, this ghost. Emotionless, calculating and guarded. When she finally looked at me, I had to turn away because her eyes were like knives cutting into my skin. With my hands still bound, I finished the juice and she vanished.

At least an hour passed while the men clicked away on their keyboards and occasionally talked into telephones about prices and locations and times. One of them picked me up and snapped a photograph, the white flash burning my eyes. It was the first time in my life that anyone had taken my picture.

The shopkeeper had cleaned the blood off his arms with paper towels and was dozing in a chair across from me when my bladder began to ache. I told the boss I had to use the bathroom, and he pointed to the kitchen. I rose and walked into the other room, then through another door in the rear.

Inside was a Western toilet, the kind they only have in nice restaurants. As I was trying to figure out what to do with my hands tied behind me, I heard the door open.

It was her. My heart began to pound.

"What's happening?" I asked quietly. "Where am I? Who are those men?"

I felt cold metal against my wrists, then heard a snap. My hands fell free and, for the first time, I saw a flash of feeling cross her face. She spoke only a single word, but it was filled with years of anger and the warning of a wise soul.

"*Run.*"

Then she was gone again. I was in shock, and a little bit scared to attempt an escape, but there was no time to waste. I retied my shoes, trying to remember how many right turns and left turns and steps and doorways had been in our path while I was blindfolded. I knew they would see me as I ran through the room, knew my escape would fail if I encountered anyone in the passages leading out to the street, or if any of the doors were locked.

I breathed deep a few times, then stepped into the kitchen. The girl was not there. From the other room, I heard a crash, glass breaking, a tray hitting the floor. I peaked around the corner and she was thrashing around at the men's feet. It looked like she was having a violent seizure, and all four men huddled around her, asking each other what to do. Their backs were to me. This must have been part of her plan.

I ran as quietly as I could to the door, and she screamed as I reached it, covering the sound of the knob twisting, the door swinging open and then shut. I was in the first hallway. Finding my way wasn't as difficult as I had expected; one passage led to another, and only once did I have to choose which way to turn. I chose correctly, and before long I reached the door leading into the garage. I peeked in and the room was empty, no one in sight, so I flipped the switch to the secret garage door, dashed across the room and rolled out into the driveway.

At the corner, I headed right because it seemed like home was that way, and once on the dim boulevard I sprinted for three blocks before I started getting winded. Then I kept sprinting. My legs felt strong, but my head and stomach hurt. I could feel the taped bandage beginning to pull away, and the stinging from the cuts made it painful to move, let alone run.

I hadn't heard anyone in pursuit when I escaped the building, but after about a minute I saw the black car speed past and skid to a stop in an alley fifty meters in front of me, blocking the sidewalk. As two of the men jumped out of the car, I heard the sound of voices on my trail. It was the shopkeeper and the boss. There was a tall, deserted building on my right that looked dangerous—the kind of place I would never go under normal circumstances. But on either side of the front door was a vertical series of small windowsills, glass broken out, that looked just big enough. The men were closing in on me and I had nowhere else to go, so I dove headfirst through the lowest window to the left of the door.

Once I was through, it was only seconds before the first man reached the door and kicked it hard enough to rattle the doorjamb. So I kept running, dodging through a maze of old, frozen machinery and plastic sheets hanging down from the ceiling. I measured the odds of outrunning four grown men, three in good shape, and decided throwing them off my trail was the only option. As I made my way to the rear of the factory, a plan started taking shape.

I knew there were several floors inside the building, but the only other time I was trying to escape in a place like this, it had been a mistake to go up. If the ground floor is the only one with exits, it is the only hope of a convincing diversion. I had been in the building less than thirty seconds, yet knew exactly what I needed to do. I'm usually not so clever—for some reason, even though I was injured and in unfamiliar territory, I was thinking more clearly. It didn't make any sense.

As I reached the back wall of the building, I heard the front door crash open. Then voices. I felt along the wall for a door, and the first one I found was locked. The knob on the next door was ready to fall off, so I grabbed it and planned what would come next. Timing was the key. There could be no mistakes.

The men were about halfway through the factory when I pulled on the doorknob. It came off easily, and I kicked the door as hard as I could. Slamming open, it let in a shaft of orange light from a street lamp outside, and I ran back inside the factory toward a stairwell about ten meters away. There was a hollow space filled with garbage beneath the first flight, garbage that I hoped would conceal me and save my life. I burrowed in and cleared a hole in front of my face so I could see.

Three of the four men reached the door around the same time, while the shopkeeper lagged behind, out of breath. The boss stuck his head out the door, then cursed and ordered his men to search the alleys behind the factory. He was furious when he turned toward the man who had knocked me out in his filthy store a couple hours earlier.

"If he goes to the police ..." His voice trailed off, trembling with emotion. He kicked a bucket, sent it flying through the cold, musty air. "He's been to the office! He knows what I look like!"

The shopkeeper cowered. Once or twice, it looked like he was about to talk, but he kept silent. The boss was staring at him like he was already trying to decide how to get rid of the body. "If we don't find him, you will have proven yourself to be a liability," he said finally, calmly. "I do not tolerate liabilities."

Five minutes later, the two men came in from the alley. "Well?" he asked. The smaller one shook his head, and the boss pulled a cylinder of black metal from his coat pocket. His right hand rose in front of him with a pistol, and he threaded the piece of metal onto the end of the gun. The shopkeeper dropped to his knees and begged for his life. He was shaking, crying, and I felt bad for him then. I didn't want him to die; I wanted him to go back to his store and keep selling cigarettes. But without a word, the man with the ponytail shot him three times in the chest, each shot echoing like a slap through the factory.

I am no stranger to hiding—I hide from my father all the time, that cheap, violent excuse for a man. Less than a week ago, he came home from losing his last Yuan at Mahjong and threw me against the television, which fell to the ground and broke into pieces. He was just getting warmed up when I dove by him, escaped onto the roof of our building and hid until morning.

Maybe you should know some things about him. I

wouldn't say there were never good times. I remember him buying me a popsicle once and smiling down at me as we walked on a summer afternoon. He brought home a bicycle for me last year, and we used to watch the news together sometimes. His fits and abuse are more common, though, and I have scars to show for it. As I've grown, he has gone from throwing me to hitting me, and I actually think I prefer to be thrown than hit. Hiding, of course, is one of my best skills after eight years of this.

But until last night, I had never hidden in a pile of trash, and I had never been in the same room as a corpse. It was all happening at once, and all I could think of is whether my father would be angry with me for being gone overnight when I finally got home. Probably will. Probably will bang me up pretty good.

I woke up to light flooding through the open doorway. The air was frigid, but I was surprisingly warm. I guess the garbage was a kind of blanket. I sat up and noticed immediately that the shopkeeper's body was gone. Could he have survived? No, I saw him lying dead for half an hour before I'd been able to sleep the night before. I got up and walked toward the doorway, where I saw drops of blood that led outside. In the alley the red dots mingled with footprints in about an inch of fresh snow until they disappeared at a pair of tire tracks.

Avoiding the blood and footprints and tracks, I left the alley and walked into a sunny morning on the boulevard—kept walking until I saw a fruit market. I crossed the road when there was a break in the stream of cars and mopeds, commuters who had no idea what crimes had happened—and almost happened—less than a mile away and eight hours ago.

It wasn't the best market, but there was fruit and I was hungry. I saw a stand of Asian pears that looked untended, and grabbed two. Hurrying away, I bit into one just as I was hit with the business end of a broom. I remember because the bristles stung my ears and neck. When I turned, there was an angry old woman about to swing again, so I threw up my hands and began apologizing. She called you guys, and I found myself in the backseat of yet another car after being hit with yet another broom—only this time, the driver was wearing a crisp uniform and a gun. He brought me here. What else can I tell you?

When Junjie had mentioned the black car and the man with the ponytail, Commissioner Chen began writing in quick, decisive strokes on a notepad, and when the story was done he picked up the phone and dispatched two cars to the old factory building. He mentioned something about a task force, a warrant and a crime syndicate. Human smuggling.

Chen's questions begin not with the ponytail and the alley and the gun and the silencer, but with the father.

"You say he bought cigarettes at that store a lot?" he asks. The boy nods. "And he always left you on the corner, but he was usually back within a few minutes?" Junjie nods again, looking sobered. "Does he ever talk about the shopkeeper?"

"Yeah, he says he likes the guy."

"I think I'm going to need to talk to your father," says the police chief. "Know where I can find him?"

The boy recites an address, and Chen picks up the receiver and dispatches another car.

"So why do you need to know all this about my father, anyway?" Junjie asks. Chen doesn't look up, doesn't answer. "Hey, mister. What does my dad have to do with this?"

The policeman stands and walks to the window, as if he is about to address the city, chastising its criminals, its evil and crooked and wayward. He sighs, crossing his arms and planting his feet.

"Son, why do you think your father left you at that store?"

"*Left* me? What do you mean?"

"He just disappeared, right? Knowing you were still waiting on the corner?"

"Well I don't know what happened."

"And the liquor man, he knew just where to take you. Knew the black car would be waiting there. That kind of meeting takes at least 24 hours to arrange."

"I don't understand."

Chen turns from the window, looking older than when Junjie had been escorted into his office. He wears an emotion the boy hasn't seen in a long time, since his mother died. Sadness.

"You don't need to. The only thing you need to understand now is that you are an orphan."

The words land like a physical blow. No boy wants to be an orphan, not even when his father is a drunk—a worthless, loveless man.

"No! No, I am not an orphan!" he shouts. "I have a father! We lost each other last night, that's all."

He is crying now, sobbing, hoping he is right. The officer sits back down behind his desk. Five minutes later, the phone rings and he picks it up, listens and sets it back down.

"He's here," says Chen, pointing toward the lobby.

He walks around the desk and grabs the doorknob, pausing while Junjie stands and wipes his eyes. The boy walks to his side and instinctively reaches up for his hand. Hanging his head, the police chief squeezes the poor boy's fingers, then opens the door.

As soon as they clear the doorway, Junjie recognizes the man in handcuffs and cries his name before he can stop himself. The suspect looks up at the child, and then at the officer beside him. Then he laughs. He looks worse than ever, hair matted and clothes torn. He looks like the one who'd spent the night in a pile of trash. A deputy unlocks his cuffs and tells him to sit down.

"Mister, is this your boy?" Chen asks him.

He looks with hollow eyes, looks Junjie over from head to toe, scratches his stubble. He glances down at his feet, then back up at Junjie. Their eyes are locked when he says it.

"No, he's not mine. I don't have a son."

What isn't said

The first ring sounds to Silas like the bell opening a boxing match. Six rings until the familiar recording, his whole family chiming, "You've reached the Kings," followed by a cheerful invitation to "leave a message, y'all." That was back in high school, during his Melissa years, when being home schooled was a mark of pride, before he knew better. Five siblings and two dedicated parents, one of whom he hopes will pick up. It happens on the fifth ring.

"Hello?"

His father sounds husky, abbreviated—that's sleep in his

voice. This is going to be worse than Silas expected.

"Hey dad," he says. A pause, a sigh.

"Do you know what time it is? This better be important."

"Dad, I'm in jail. Down here in Lexington. I need help."

"And?"

Silas leans his forehead against the cool block wall.

"Bail's $10,000. I need you to come post for me."

"Son, I have never posted bail for anybody in my life. Why would I start now?"

"I understand, I'm sorry to ask you to do this. But if you don't help me I'm going to be in here all weekend."

Silence on the line. That's a good sign, Silas thinks to himself. He's considering it.

"Why were you arrested?"

"A guy at the bar was messing with this girl I know from one of my classes, and I—"

"What did you do? What are you charged with?"

"Assault and battery," Silas answers. "I hit him and the whole place erupted."

"Are you hurt?"

"Not bad, just a tap on the nose." Macho was a defining characteristic of the new self, the manly identity that Silas had slipped on like a familiar leather coat when he got to the University of Kentucky. "I need to wash up, but I'm fine."

Dad sighs again, and Silas hears pent-up disappointment in what isn't said.

"I'm sure not going to drive all the way down there to get you out tonight," he says eventually.

"But dad—"

"I don't want to hear it, Silas. You made it clear to your mother and I that you're on your own down there. Funny how independence is only cool when it's convenient. You're going to spend the night in jail; it'll be good for you. I'll drive down before church—on one condition: You're coming back to Florence with me. We're going to talk."

Silas tries to ask if his mother is awake, but the line goes dead. So that's what the one phone call thing is like. A police officer waves him back to the holding cell, and Silas reaches up to feel his nose. There's dried blood on his upper lip and several large stains on the bright blue shirt he was given on his first day as a bouncer. It was a proud moment, and he had looked forward to wearing the word SECURITY on his back every weekend. Being fired for assaulting a customer—not so proud.

But the phone call, that was the ultimate humiliation. As if he needed reminding of his father's strict ideas of absolute sobriety and above-reproach living, ninety minutes in the truck tomorrow morning would be a refresher, of sorts. The only thing less appealing, he thought, was having to sit in jail until Monday morning's arraignment. Just in case, he thought, it might not be unwise to make nice with the guard.

"Hey, did you hear the one about the priest, the minister and the rabbi?" he asks over his shoulder.

"Yeah, I heard it," the guard says. "It's called shut up and get in the cell."

"That's actually not how it goes," Silas replies, hoping for a smirk, a grin, a little banter—something.

Nothing. The joyless officer clanks the noisy gate open and stands aside while Silas maneuvers his wide, 6'4" frame into the cell. Inside, he looks around for a seat; the only one is between two of the worst-looking characters—a drunk who is single-handedly stinking up the room and a talkative, wiry dude with the unnatural energy of a hardcore druggie. He sits down between them and leans his head back against the bars, wondering why he couldn't just let his classmate in the bar fend for herself.

He knows the answer: it's his upbringing. Silas was raised to scorn drunkards and druggies, and here he is, in a jail cell, wedged between one of each for fighting, which was also considered a serious breach of self-control in his family.

But chivalry is there, too. It lingers in the confusion of theories and experiences he calls an identity.

Family was always important to Silas. Even now, he considers himself a good brother, although he hasn't been home since before his sophomore year started last fall. He skipped Christmas because he landed his job as a bouncer on the condition that he would fill shifts during the short-handed holidays. In his free time he plays basketball and works out. Hours at the gym are required to maintain the muscle he has added since high school to his imposing frame.

Silas before college was polite and gentle. Silas during college
is loud and popular, nicknamed "Ace" for his exceptional talent
at poker—yet another taboo hobby in his Southern Baptist clan.
He does well in his classes, not for effort but for aptitude. He
barely invests himself in the classroom because he doesn't consider himself a student. He's more like royalty in his own world—
true to his last name, King—and the campus is his kingdom.

His ego pushes the envelope with teachers, with his employ-
er, even with friends. But all his new university friends were o-
riginally drawn to him for his prowess, so it was to be expected.
He is athletically talented, smart and masculine—and he knows
it. And he lets everyone else know it. He takes advantage of
everything college life has to offer, stopping short of drugs and
crime.

Girls were the other exception. Everyone assumed he was a
player, but his father and grandfathers had successfully drilled into him a respect for women that he secretly nurtured. His ex-
girlfriend, Mel, had also played a part in shaping his courtesy toward women. She was the one thing about high school he missed
when he shed his small-town persona on his way to Lexington.

The university was the first place Silas had found respect for
the things he wanted people to admire about him. Back home, in
Florence, folks would compliment his patience, his loyalty.
"What a good brother," they'd say. "What a nice boy." It was
always "boy." Even Mel used the word on him.

"What do want me to call you?" she had asked in the first

moments of their break-up. "My *man-friend?*"

But here in Lexington, even the toughest, most territorial guys gave Ace a wide berth. You were likely to hear him described as "one mean dude." Never "a nice boy."

Silas didn't expect jail to be comfortable, but he wasn't ready for how harsh it was. After a few minutes, his head begins to throb where it's resting against the bars, and try as he might to avoid touching his neighbors, his size requires it. He already smells like a drunk, tired and bloodied, utterly defeated.

He rubs his jaw, which started hurting since he sat down, and his hip, which apparently was kicked during the ruckus. As he kneads his side and lower back, he feels a wad of cash he won at poker before work. He had moved the money from his pocket to his waist band back at the bar, hoping it wouldn't be found and confiscated on his way into the city jail.

Without thinking, he pulls it out, imagining for a second that he could cover his own bail. But then he remembers it is only $1,200—by far his biggest pot, but well short of the $10,000 required to waltz out of jail. Usually his winnings are less than $100, so he is not used to carrying this much money. Cash in hand, he's managed to get the attention of everyone in the cell who's not asleep.

"Maaan, you know how much dope you could buy with that?" the druggie on his right asks, fidgeting closer to Silas. "That's like, that's like at least, like at least—I could go for a week—no! Well, yeah, OK, at least a week, a solid week!"

Silas returns the bills to the deepest part of his pocket and stares sideways at him.

"What?"

"Hey man, don't judge—don't you judge a poor man's habits. I'm just sayin', with a little bread like that—I mean, if I had even half—if I had twenty bucks right when I got out of this place, right after I buy myself a pizza, then I could do some damage. Man, a pizza sounds good right now."

Silas shakes his head.

"Was that English?"

The cellmate clicks his tongue, feigning insult. "Man, you ain't no better than me, OK?"

"*OK,*" Silas replies, rolling his eyes.

"It's like this—'cuz I been here before, lots of times before. I practically been livin' here. So it's like this. I don't care who you is out there," he says, jabbing his arm between the bars, "but in here, right here, on this bench, you and me, we equals." He raises his chin in the air like a philosopher.

Silas cocks his head toward him.

"*We* are not equals," he answers.

"We equals," says a low voice from the other side of the cell. It's attached to a big man with tattoos of flames and skulls climbing his scalp. Arms crossed, he is glaring at Silas.

Nothing more is said; nothing more needs saying. Against his better judgment, Silas allows himself sleep, and the first thing he sees in his dreams is a fist that lands on his cheek. His subconscious is replaying the fight back at the bar.

The blow to his face had been the first act in a melee that would go down as legend in Lexington. Silas had watched a man harass the girl from math class for at least ten minutes from his place at the door. The middle - aged lush had gotten bolder and closer, despite her attempts to rebuff him. Then he crossed the line of physical contact, reaching around her waist. Silas nodded to another bouncer to take over at the door while he handled it.

He could have been a little gentler, a little more subtle. But in place of the annoyance he usually felt when peeling a drunk off a girl, there was only rage. With every step, he felt it building, and when he saw the man advance again on the struggling girl, his pace quickened. He knocked several people out of the way in the last twenty feet and pinned the offending drunk a- gainst the bar. Seconds later he was hit from the side, and the rest was destiny.

Silas shook off the punch, which came from an accomplice, and tossed the man in his grip over the nearest table as he spun. The one who had hit him was edging closer, fists up. Two more friends emerged from the crowd that was melting away into a circle.

As Silas was staring down the three men, he felt the original drunk—a small, thin man—jump onto his back and slip a sloppy choke hold around his neck. Immediately, the second attacker moved in, but was met with a boot in the chest that sent him reeling onto the dance floor with broken ribs and the wind knocked out of him.

Silas made quick work of the pair in front of him. The first one caught an uppercut that took him off his feet, and the second was hit in the stomach as with a sledgehammer. He doubled over as Silas brought his knee up to meet his face, landing with a crunch; the only man left conscious was the one on his back.

In one motion, he swung his right leg out in front of him, then jumped with his left, going horizontal in the air. From six feet high, he landed on the drunk with all his weight. Clearly not wanting any more of Silas, the man let go and began stammering a plea for mercy. But it was too late for that.

The huge bouncer rose with the man's foot in his hand, dragging him toward the door. The crowd parted, and when he reached the entrance he pulled hard on the offender's leg, lifting him off the ground and flipping him onto the sidewalk like a bag of dog food. He thudded to the pavement and Silas turned back into the tavern only to be hit squarely on the nose. By then the whole place was in the throes of an epic bar fight, and it lasted another twenty minutes before the police arrived to sort things out.

As the scene replays in Silas' dream, he is restless, twitching in his place on the cell bench. No one is awake except the tweaker on his right, who is increasingly worried by the big man's movements. Suddenly Silas elbows him in the shoulder, slamming his back against the bars and sending an echo through the cell block. It's enough to rouse Silas from his dream, and he finds his kinetic neighbor poised to strike.

"Hey man!" shouts the cellmate. "What're you tryin' to do, man? You tryin' to get us both locked up?!"

Silas shakes off the sleep and squints.

"We're already locked up, genius."

"I don't care if we are, don't care at all. I'll tangle with you any day—uh, night. Or day, yeah! Any day, anywhere. You don't scare me."

"I don't want to fight," Silas mumbles, too exhausted to keep up. The cellmate doesn't hear him.

"I'll fight you!" he presses, jabbing the air.

"I said I don't want to fight."

"OK, I guess I'll let you off. Just this once. I know karate anyways," he adds with satisfaction. "Wouldn't be fair."

Silas spends the rest of the night awake and silence prevails for hours, until the middle of the night, when the guard comes for someone named Aloysius Reese. One of the inmates throws his shoe at the drunk man on Silas' left, who jolts awake and lets out a string of expletives that lasts until he sees the guard standing at the open gate. Another few hours and the guard returns, this time reading Silas' name off the clipboard.

"Silas King!" he says, jamming a key into the gate. "Someone named Edward is here to post your bail."

The young man stands up, sore and ornery, and follows the officer down to the counter, where his father is counting out $10,000 in cash. The guard motions him into the lobby, and he goes, walking up next to his dad.

"This is Sophie's college money," Ed says without looking up.

"You're going to let Sophie go away to college?" Silas replies.

"Not if she turns out like you."

The cashier snorts, looking Silas over. Besides the blood stains, his shirt is torn in several places, including the right sleeve, which is ripped just high enough to reveal one of his tattoos—four aces. Spades, diamonds, clubs, hearts. The money counted, Silas and his father sign papers and walk out the front door toward the family's '78 Chevy pickup, parked curbside in front of the station. The early sun is heating up the moist air outside.

Silas doesn't know whether to expect a long, quiet ride, a lecture, or a blitz of anger and criticism. They climb into the cab, each rolling down his window immediately. The air is already warm, as June air often is in the morning in Kentucky, and Silas is relieved to be out. He decides to break the silence.

"Dad, I know how this looks," he says plaintively. "I know you think it's a result of all my choices you disapprove of."

"Like working in a bar," Ed says flatly.

"It's a job," Silas shrugs.

"The only one in Lexington?"

"Well, no, but a good-paying one for a big guy. And it's not like I can drink while I'm working, or party, or socialize. When I'm at work, I'm working."

"Bible says blessed is the man who walks not in the counsel of the ungodly, nor stands in the path of sinners. What does a bouncer do? Stands in the path of a bunch of idiots fixin' to get drunk and cheat on their wives."

"What about 'being in the world'?"

"Don't church-talk me, son," he says, shooting Silas an angry look. "When was the last time you went, anyway?"

"I don't know."

"Well, you're going today."

"What? Wait, no, I can't show up at church like this. Look at me."

"Yeah, I seen your new look back at the precinct," says Ed, cracking a grin for the first time. "But I'm driving, and your mother's meeting us there with the kids."

"Aw, dad, I really just want to go home and sleep. Don't I at least deserve a nap?"

"Deserve?"

Wrong word, Silas thinks to himself.

"*Deserve?!* Kid, you don't deserve anything but to sit in that cell back there until they decide how much community service you get to do. The fact I came and got you is your mother's do-ing. I'd a left you."

The air roaring in the windows makes him yell louder as they speed north on I-75; the small cab amplifies the earful Silas is receiving.

"And while we're talking about what you deserve and don't

deserve, let me make one thing crystal clear. I will not pay any more of your tuition until you convince me you got your head on right. Not one more dime. So if you want to keep living it up in Lexington this fall, you better grow up this summer. And I mean quick."

He hits the steering wheel with his palm to punctuate the last word, shifting in his seat. There are a lot of things Silas wants to say, but nothing he should. So he rides in silence while his father reloads. It takes about ten minutes.

"You know, son, you have a lot of potential. You're my firstborn. I want to be proud of you, I want to brag on you to the other dads at church. All their kids look up to you, and if there's anything worse than how you treat your family, it's what a waste you're making of your God-given abilities."

"Maybe God's given me some abilities you just can't deal with," Silas answers.

"Like what? Gambling? Womanizing?"

"I could have been good at football, but you wouldn't let me play."

The older man runs his fingers through hair. "Actually, that was your mother," he says. "I thought you'd have been good, too."

Another few minutes of silence. The scenery is changing as Lexington grows distant; the day is changing again—warm to hot. It's bright outside, and traffic is sparse. Just a few big rigs.

"Dad, are we ever going to understand each other? I mean,

I just don't share a lot of your convictions—they're not practical in the real world."

"What do you know about the real world?" It's the first question that actually sounds like a question, instead of an insult. "Really, Silas. Besides that vacation to the West Coast back in 2003, you haven't left the Midwest. My rules may be outdated, but in the real world they'll steer you true."

"I don't know," Silas mumbles, resigned to the idea of never seeing eye to eye with his parents.

"It's hard when your kids reject your values. You'll understand someday."

Another fifteen minutes and the pickup sputters off the interstate, heading toward Florence First Southern Baptist Church.

"We're running early," says Ed, sounding considerably calmer than when they got in the truck. "I'll swing by the fillin' station so you can wash up a bit."

It's all familiar to Silas—the smell of Florence, the corner gas station, the water tower. Striped in red and white, the huge tank had originally advertised a local mall, but violated regulations and had to be hastily repainted. City workers erased the two outer lines in the letter "M," added an apostrophe and now it just says "Florence Y'all."

Silas walks through the worn double doors at the station and approaches the counter. A scraggly cashier peeks over the lottery tickets and laughs.

"Look who's come home from the city to grace us with his

presence. What's up, big guy?"

"Hey Mo. What are you doing down there?"

"Oh, you know, just organizing my babies."

"You still into those? You know that fad went out like ten years ago, right?"

"Beanies ain't no fad!" Mo replies, pronouncing each word emphatically, like a drumbeat. He shakes his head and disappears below the counter again, muttering about fads and "big smart guys who go off to college."

"Mo, I need the bathroom key," Silas says. The cashier points to a stick hanging next to the cash register, and Silas heads around the back of the store. He washes his face and bald head, freshly shaven the previous morning. In the cracked mirror, he looks at himself for the first time since getting out of jail.

"Real world," he says under his breath. "Equals."

He walks back into the store and grabs a stick of deodorant on his way to the counter.

"First time you ever washed blood off your face in my store," Mo says, leaning his fists on the counter. "Was it bad?"

"I got fired," Silas says. "Spent the night locked up."

"And then had to call your dad to bail you out," Mo adds, peering past Silas to the old Chevy at the pump. He whistles. "That must have been fun."

"Worst part," Silas says, grinning. "You have a shirt I could borrow?"

"Nothin' that would fit you," says the cashier, holding up his hands as if to measure the young man's shoulders.

"OK then, see you later," he says, turning to leave. "I'll hit you back for the deodorant."

"Don't worry about it," Mo replies, pinching his nose and scowling. "Consider it my contribution to society."

Five minutes later, the old Chevy swings into the church parking lot, pulling alongside the family's other vehicle, a navy blue cargo van. Siblings are piling out into the humid morning air. They see Silas and start whispering. Brothers wave excitedly, sisters frown their disapproval.

"Here we go," Ed says and cuts the engine.

The first person to approach Silas is his mother, a petite, fit woman in her late forties. She looks distressed, worse than the time a tornado took out her herb garden and damaged the roof. She's obviously been up all night, probably fretting more about what the Sunday school ladies will say than about Silas, he thinks to himself. She hurries up to him and reaches for his face; he bends down.

"Look at you," she says, voice cracking. "Are you hurt?"

"No, mom. Just a couple bruises."

"You got in a fight, didn't you?" pipes up the second-to-youngest brother, earning a swat on the head from the eldest sister. He and the two other boys start walking toward the church, arguing about fights and how long Silas would last against various TV wrestlers. The three sisters huddle quietly by the van, pretending to ignore Silas.

After a brief health questionnaire, Silas' mother is satisfied he's going to survive. She puts her hands on her hips and is about to begin her carefully planned verbal assault when Ed cuts in.

"I've already said everything you're about to say, and more," he tells her. "Let's just go to church."

She redirects her offensive.

"Are you serious? He can't go in looking like this." She points to his torn polo shirt, then sniffs in his direction. "Or smelling like he does."

"Hey!" he objects, suddenly an observer at his own trial. "I put on deodorant."

"Stay out of this," his dad snaps. "Do you have any idea the last time he went to church? He's going in."

"No, he is not!" she answers, lowering her voice to a whisper. "Do you want our friends to see him like this?"

"It's not about our friends," he says angrily. "And it's not about you!"

"Oh, I should have guessed. It's about you, of course."

"Woman—"

"It's OK, dad, I'll wait out here," Silas offers.

"You're going in," Ed says with finality, looking from wife to son and back.

Silas walks toward his sisters and nods at the church; they proceed in front of their parents.

"All right, everyone, let's be happy," their mother chirps, clapping twice. "This is church!"

Everything is as he remembered: Stained glass windows, tan carpet, bulletin boards on every wall with photos of vacation Bible school and youth group retreats. He's in some of the snapshots, plus a full head of hair and minus tattoos. The low entry leads into a tall but modest sanctuary, where folks are seeking out their usual seats.

Silas is taking it all in for the first time in ten months when he hears a familiar voice behind him.

"Looks like *security* had a rough night," she says. He spins.

"Mel, wow. How are you?"

"I'm OK," she says. "Probably doing a little better than you, from the looks of it."

"Oh yeah, well, it's kind of a long story," he says. "And it seems like you're pretty busy."

Mel is carrying an armful of fliers, and wearing a T-shirt that says something about summer camp on it. It's tied in a knot at her hip, and she's wearing jeans and sandals. As they talk, she hands pamphlets to parishioners. She throws in a DVD for anyone who seems interested. The people who don't recognize Silas stare openly until he notices; those who remember him either pretend they don't or attempt an awkward "hello." Mel smiles at everyone except Silas, with whom she hasn't actually made eye contact yet. He remembers that smile. Devastating.

"Is that blood on your shirt?" she says as the stream of people thins. She turns, scandalized. "It is. It's blood. Were you in a *fight?*"

"Like I said, long story," he answers, hoping to avoid a scene.

"Summarize," she presses.

"I'd rather not."

She blinks, surprised.

"Um. OK, sorry," she says, returning to the card table where her promotional materials are piled. "Nice catching up with you."

"Mel, I'll tell you all about it, just not here," he says, following her across the lobby. "My family's already embarrassed enough."

She nods, tidying stacks of fliers on the table. "I can understand that." She pauses, looks into his eyes for the first time. "Same new Silas."

"C'mon, let's not go there again," he says. "You haven't seen me in almost a year."

"And your first time back, you walk into church looking like you spent the night in jail."

He shifts his weight and looks away.

"Are you *serious?*" she says, reading his body language. She scoffs; he winces and hangs his head.

"Dad posted bail for me this morning. That's why I'm here, like this."

"What are you thinking? Is this place a joke to you? Your hometown? Your church?"

He leans against the wall and looks around.

"It's not my church anymore."

"Too small for you?"

"No, I've just moved on," he says.

"Well, so have I," she snaps. "So. Was there something else?"

He lifts a brochure off the card table and opens it. Dozens of Asian children are pictured with Americans, on water slides, coloring, dancing. There are photos of the Great Wall, Tiananmen Square, but mostly of children. They look happy. Everyone looks happy.

"Is this what you're doing this summer?" he asks.

"Yes."

He looks at her, waiting for more.

"And?" he asks.

"And what? It's a group from California that does summer camp for Chinese orphans. I'm going for two weeks next month."

"Is it expensive?"

"Airfare, mostly."

"How much is that?" he asks.

"$1,200."

The opening music in the sanctuary is receding, and Silas' father enters the lobby headed for the men's room.

"Get in there, Silas," he says. "I didn't bring you down here to harass Melissa the whole time."

Mel smiles, leaning to see around Silas. "Good morning, Mr.

King."

Silas turns toward the sanctuary. He's still holding the brochure.

"Can I keep this?" he asks. She nods. "It's good to see you, Mel."

She doesn't answer.

Silas tries to slip unnoticed to the pew his family is monopolizing against the far right wall, but he can feel the stares. Even the pastor watches him for a few seconds while he begins his sermon. He sits down next to his mom, and a minute later his father joins them. Silas turns and whispers.

"Dad, you've been to China, right?"

Ed nods impatiently.

"What was it like?"

As far back as the stories go

For hours on end during the long train ride home, Lien-Hua had agonized over how to begin teaching English to the children in her hometown, a village of 500 tucked in green mountains and split by a wide, slow river. She had considered starting with the mechanics, how English plays fast and loose with its own rules, where to place verbs and adjectives for maximum effectiveness. Ultimately, she had decided on a single word.

"Forever," she says, pronouncing the syllables clearly, with authority. And again: "For-ev-er." An American would have noticed her slight difficulty with the R, the common slow twisting of the sound that she's been trying to cure at the university. But here, in the tiny village, no one knows the difference. To them Lien-Hua is a perfect example of academic success, speaking this strange English like it's second nature, and learning things—very important things—she could bring home and share with the rest of the town, sequestered in one of the most scenic regions of China.

It is a bright, warm day in the mountains northwest of Chengdu, capital of Sichuan province. Lien-Hua loves being at the university, with its impressive buildings and wide paved streets, but nothing compares to the lush forests and slow-moving streams of her hometown. Here, mountains tower as they have for all of history. The peaks and ridges have cut a horizon in the same pattern for generations, as far back as the stories go.

Forever.

Fifteen students stare up at Lien-Hua, puzzled.

"What does it mean?" asks a boy in the front row.

"That will come later," she answers firmly. "For now, just say it with me."

They practice together, eight repetitions, just like her professor always demanded back at college. The children learn the basic sounds of the word easily, and again press for a definition. Lien-Hua explains, then returns to the lesson. The old farming shed behind her family's house is packed with students, none of whom have ever heard a single syllable of English until this morning. When Lien-Hua's parents had spread the word that their daughter would be teaching, and that her class would only hold fifteen boys and girls, the list had filled within an hour.

A few hundred feet behind a modest home surrounded by rice paddies and hillside tobacco fields, the shed is emptier than it used to be—just a few tools and a traditional harness for the old mule that's out to pasture. The doors are closed to shield the children from the distractions of a beautiful spring day—there's learning to be accomplished, and Lien-Hua won't have her first attempt at teaching undone by springtime. They continue.

"Forever is a noun," she says. "A noun can be an object, person or place. In this case, it's an idea."

Her students give her their full attention, repeating strange words and wondering when they will ever have the chance to use their newly acquired phrases. The lesson stretches an hour and a half into the bright morning, then she dismisses the class until the following day. The boy in the front row and his little sister stay behind.

"Lien-Hua, tell us what the university is like," he asks.

She sits on an upturned bucket and thinks.

"You've been to Chengdu?" she asks the lad. He nods.

"Well, Beijing is similar because it has many tall buildings and a lot of traffic. Only it is so much bigger, and there are national monuments everywhere—the Forbidden City, Tiananmen Square. It is cold in the winter and hot in the summer—"

"No, I want to know about the university," he presses. "What is it like to go to class every day, to learn from a professor?"

She laughs. He is a keen boy, one of her favorite in the village since he was little. Now eleven, he is spirited and clever, a sure bet to follow in her footsteps and attend a university someday. Perhaps he will become a doctor, or a famous engineer, helping to build the country's great dams and bridges. Or maybe he will never leave the village, in which case Lien-Hua predicts he will grow up to become one of its leaders, wise and respected.

"It is a privilege," she tells him. "Learning from such intelligent men and women is thrilling, but there is a lot of pressure, too."

The boy's sister is restless, bored by talk of school and musty old professors.

"I want to know more about the city," she says. "Are there many beautiful women there?"

Lien-Hua smiles at the girl, taking her hands and pulling her to her feet.

"Yes, there are," she tells her. "And they go to fancy restaurants every weekend, and eat expensive food, and dance."

The two girls are twirling around the old shed when a low rumbling rises to their ears from beneath the ground. It sounds like an approaching train, or a prolonged explosion miles beneath the earth, moving quickly toward the surface. As it grows louder, they pause to listen, and when it reaches a crescendo the small building begins to sway over their heads.

Shovels, rakes and other long-handled tools tip over at the

back of the shed. The swaying gives way to violent shaking, as a hard jolt knocks them off their feet. Within moments, the ground is moving as if someone had picked up the small building by its foundation and was rocking it side to side. Cracks appear in the cement pillars supporting several heavy beams. Lien-Hua shouts for the kids to follow her and instinctively dives for the door, throwing her weight against it and knocking it off its rusty hinges. She tumbles into the field as the earthquake intensifies, and while she is landing she hears a shrill metallic tearing as the roof of the shed twists and collapses.

She spins on the trembling ground in time to see the door frame implode onto the girl's lower back, pinning her hips and legs inside. Her brother is gone.

Lien-Hua is overwhelmed by the surreal sights and sounds. The trees on every mountain are shaking madly. Boulders are crashing down the steepest slopes and frightened birds fill the air. Some of the hills are even toppling, altering the topography as if it was a landscape of water. That is the only possible comparison—it's like being on rough waters, a sinking ship, a life raft— except this is dry land. She's seen nothing like it in her whole life. In the moments since the ground started shaking, the movement has only grown more severe.

A shriek knocks her out of the stupor. The younger student, who had momentarily passed out, is squirming against the debris pinning her lower body. Lien-Hua crawls to the girl's side and covers her small torso with her own, whispering to stay calm, hold still.

"We'll get you out," she says. "I'll get you out."

For the next ten minutes, the south Chinese foothills harbor an atmosphere of violence and extreme turmoil. In the distance, Lien - Hua can hear people screaming in pain, shouting names, wailing fresh grief. She always thought an earthquake would sub-side in moments, but this one seems determined to shake the country's skin off its bones. Heavy trees crack apart and slam to the ground; smoke and dust rise over collapsed buildings, and still it shakes.

Both Lien-Hua and her young, half-buried student are sob-bing, both knowing the worst had come to the boy. For the uni-versity student with plans to become a teacher, regret is instant and paralyzing: her improvised classroom imperiling her first students. For the girl, paralysis would take a different form. They grip each other and Lien-Hua cries out, "How long can it last?"

The answer comes in a small voice beneath her: "Forever."

Thirty days earlier, Lien-Hua was cramming for finals at the university—a tough English exam would join biology and early childhood education to dominate the last week of her sophomore year. While at school, tests were all that mattered: Her future depended on passing, and the hopes of her village depended, in part, on her future. For weeks at a time, immense pressure kept her studying late into the night, until numbers and symbols and theories consumed her thoughts and filled her dreams.

At 18, she had already made her parents proud by bringing home perfect report cards. In a tight - knit community rarely visited by outsiders, anything imported—including knowledge— was expected to be shared. Every time Lien - Hua had trekked home for a holiday, the night of her return had resembled a game show, as dozens of villagers gathered in the center of town to quiz her on the latest news from the capital or test her ever -expanding English vocabulary.

Less than two years after marrying, Lien-Hua's parents had conceived. Her father was hoping for a boy, someone to work the farm when senility claimed his muscles and mind, but was more than satisfied with a little girl to cradle. The farm would find a way to be worked; he was in love with his daughter and told her often he would not trade her for the strongest, proudest son.

Among other things, Lien-Hua's father had passed on his love of the morning. Often they would rise together and climb the top of the nearest hill to watch the sun glint into the sky. For eight days every spring, and eight days in the fall, the sun would rise in the crease of a steep valley east of a pinnacle she and her father called Sunrise Peak. Those were the weeks when he would plant and harvest, the lucky weeks. It was a family tradition that reached back as far as anyone could remember, which at last count was fourteen generations.

Most of the 500 people in the village could recite similar traditions and history, and no one considered it unusual to be so connected to the past. Heritage was the way of life.

But limitations were also abundant in the village. Lifestyles were lean, there were no fancy clothes or ceremonies. Sometimes there were fireworks to mark the Chinese New Year, but more often there was just an audience of stars, scattered like the remnant sparks of a great celestial celebration. Currency only ever changed hands within the village—replenishments of crisp new hundred-Yuan notes were rare, and thus the fragile supply of bills was treated carefully. Produce and raw materials were the more common currency.

For an intelligent young girl eager to learn and travel, such a community was stifling. Knowing everyone's name meant everyone knew hers, and meeting strangers was one thing Lien-Hua longed to experience. It wasn't until she had spent a month on campus that she longed to see familiar faces again, missing the local gossip and exhortation of the women as they scrubbed the week's laundry in the river.

Out of her yearnings for home, a plan took shape: After graduating in two years, she would move back to her village and start a school. Her father had rallied the men in town to pledge a new schoolhouse in replacement of the dilapidated shack behind her family's home. Doubling as a community classroom, the shed was where she had learned to read and write, where she spent years preparing for the university entrance exam—which she

took in Chengdu, the nearest big city, and passed at the top of
her testing group.

That paved the way to Beijing, and on her seventeenth birth-
day, her father had fetched a dusty jar from a shelf, spun off the
cap and dumped several rolls of hundred-Yuan notes on the table.

"I saved your grandfather's inheritance," her father said,
grinning proudly. "And your mother and I have been adding to
it ever since you decided to go to college. It should be e-
nough—hopefully those big - city eggheads haven't raised the
rates too high for a poor farmer's daughter."

Word had spread quickly: Lien-Hua was only the third villager—and the first girl—to be on her way to a university. As
her departure neared, friends and neighbors had unknowingly
raised the stakes for the young woman until the pressure was e-
normous. The morning she left with her father for the train station in Chengdu, the townsfolk raised a banner with a clear
mandate: MAKE US PROUD!

Classes flew by, trips home had been sweet and supportive,
and then the plans for a village school took shape. While she was
enjoying life in Beijing, learning its boulevards, plazas and parks
by heart, Lien-Hua sought out opportunities to work with children and practice English. One day, her roommate mentioned
an American group hosting summer camps for orphans.

"They bring the children to play games and sing and feel like
part of a family for a week," the older student had told her.

"You can practice both English and teaching if you go."

She had emailed the camp director, an Australian named Douglas who in turn set up a telephone interview with an American. The day of the scheduled phone call was rainy, and Lien-Hua walked half a mile across campus to arrive an hour early at the computer lab. The only time in her life she had been more nervous was when she sat down for the college entrance exam. At the computer lab, she checked her email and was waiting by a bank of telephones against the wall, clothes still damp, when one of the worn sets rang.

"Is this Lien-Hua?" came a cheerful voice, slightly mispronouncing her name.

"Lien-Hua, yes," she said. "Who is this?"

"This is Melissa. I work for Bring Me Hope, and I am interviewing potential translators for camp this summer in Nanchang."

Lien-Hua paused; an unknown word had slipped by. "Sorry— what kind of translators?"

"Huh?"

"What?" A delay on the line was playing tricks on Lien-Hua's ear. She began to feel flustered as her words ran together with her interviewer's. "You say you were interview some kind for translators. I don't understand."

"Oh, I said 'potential' translators," Melissa said, giggling.

"What means potential?" Lien-Hua asked.

"It means, like, maybe," said Melissa.

They talked for half an hour, until Lien-Hua was forced to

make room for several other students waiting to call home.

"Well, you are a very kind girl," Melissa said. "And your English is strong. I will send you an email to confirm if you are selected as a translator."

"Confirm?" Lien-Hua repeated.

"It means more than maybe," she answered. "For sure."

When Lien-Hua returned to the dormitory, her roommate asked how it went. She was soaked from a second long walk in the rain, but beaming—mostly from the thrill of her first international conversation.

"It went well, I think," she answered in Chinese, then in English: "More-than-maybe!"

The night before her final exams, Lien-Hua slipped on her shoes and headed toward the computer lab, because email was a luxury worth walking across campus to enjoy. She loved every bit of it: Logging in, clicking the keys, and seeing words from a friend or classmate materialize on the screen. This night, she was hoping for a very important message; if it hadn't arrived, she would have to assume she wasn't accepted as a summer camp translator.

It was there, hovering in her inbox, beckoning. Her pulse quickened as she read. "I am happy to inform you that you have been accepted as a translator. Please be in Nanchang during the first week of July." She jotted down the instructions in a small pink notebook, then started back to her room, elated and nervous.

What were orphans like? What did she have to offer them? It

would be a few more weeks until the Sichuan earthquake; skipping down the stairs and out into the cool night air, she realized that she had not experienced much pain, nor encountered it in others. Sad, rejected children were especially foreign. She hoped she would be able to relate.

As the ground shifts and shudders beneath Lien - Hua, she places a knee on the earth, then rises to her feet, only to be upended by a powerful jolt. She has forgotten Beijing and its classrooms, its wide streets and tourists. All that matters is survival. Still gripped by terror and awe, she starts pulling at the rubble of her parents' shed, tossing small chunks of concrete and wood over her shoulder and clawing at larger pieces until they come loose.

Lien-Hua's father appears around the corner of the family's house, moving with speed over the uneven ground. He sees his daughter and shouts for joy, then spots the girl trapped at her feet and rushes to help. Chest heaving, he explains between breaths that he had been across town haggling with a rival rice farmer when the quake hit. As they work, the first tremor subsides, but aftershocks are frequent and sudden, shaking almost as violently as the original.

"Mother was in the back room having tea," he said, abbreviating every few words with a gasp of air. He works even more quickly than Lien-Hua to move the debris. "The four of us made it back to the open field behind their house. All I could think about was getting over here to find you." He pauses and grasps her arm. "Where is the boy—her brother?"

Lien-Hua's head drops, her shoulders tremble. He gathers her into his arms and closes his eyes, but comfort is a luxury that would have to wait. He smoothes her thick black hair and kisses her cheek. "It's not your fault," he says over and over. "Lien-Hua, go tend to your mother in the house. She is hurt, but she will survive. And the house is damaged, but we can repair it. I will dig the little one out and join you."

Twelve minutes later, he bursts through the front door carrying the girl.

"She can't walk," he says, setting her down gingerly on the kitchen table, where hot tea and dumplings were served just that morning. "Can't feel her toes."

Lien-Hua rushes to her side, reaching for her hand and cradling the girl's head. "I'm sorry," she says. "I'm so sorry."

The girl is barely conscious, too shocked to feel, although there are trails where tears have cut through the dust on her pretty face.

"He made me go first," she tells Lien-Hua. "He said there was time for us both to get out."

The young teacher buries her face in the girl's torn dress, then looks up at her with red eyes.

"I'm so sorry," she repeats. "I never would have—"

The girl places a finger across Lien-Hua's lips and nods.

Across the room, the old man is clearing debris off the family's spare bed when his wife, Lien-Hua's mother, asks about the child's brother. He shakes his head.

"What about her parents?" she presses. "Shouldn't we get them over here?"

He shakes his head again. "Saw their house on the way over. What used to be their house." He lowers his voice to a whisper. "I'd be surprised if anyone on that side of town survived," he said, motioning toward the neighborhood nestled up to the base of a steep slope. Several boulders bigger than houses had decimated the area, landing like bombs and issuing a series of deafening explosions that rocked the village at the height of the earthquake. As he speaks, an aftershock rumbles underfoot and the three adults scramble to get outside with the injured girl.

"We'll have to stay outdoors," he says, inspecting a web of hundreds of paper-thin cracks spreading across the plaster walls of their home.

Lien-Hua spends the rest of the afternoon sitting by the girl's side, caressing her face and rinsing the dust off her limbs. In a flash, she has forgotten a lifetime of solace and been initiated into the fiercest of the world's violence and sorrow. The town, her town, which she had grown up loving, then scorned, then rediscovered, is a war zone. At some point, her father leaves to join the able-bodied men in a crudely organized search and rescue effort. Fires need extinguishing, families need reuniting. Everywhere, people need triage and more—surgery and blood transfusions that won't arrive for two weeks.

Darkness falls on that scene having worsened, if anything. And

Lien-Hua drifts to sleep curled up next to the injured girl. No dreams tonight.

Her body feels heavy and sore when she is awoken before sunrise. Her father, looking defeated and haggard, whispers an invitation to Sunrise Peak.

"It's lucky week," he says. "Sunrise in the valley."

She doesn't want to go, doesn't want to move. She doesn't want to leave the meadow beside their house, nor smell the smoke, nor enter the disheveled forest, nor hear the weeping she knows hasn't stopped all night. But her father insists.

"I haven't slept," he tells her. "I need to watch the sunrise, then I can rest an hour or two."

The air is cool as they thread their way through the trees toward the nearest mountaintop. Fallen trunks and limbs obstruct the trail, and the predawn noises commonly heard in the spring are gone. The birds have wisely left in search of safer branches.

It takes twice as long to reach the top, but they arrive with fifteen minutes to spare, sitting on the same rock they have shared since Lien-Hua was a toddler, which is remarkably unmoved after the previous day's earthquake. Father and daughter sit in silence while the gray passes shades toward pink, then crimson. Finally a wedge of sun appears in the tip of the valley. Lien-Hua breaks the silence.

"I'm not going back to school," she says. "I'm staying here to help rebuild."

Her father doesn't reply, doesn't move. He stares at the jagged horizon and inhales deeply. The light shifts; the whole sun is now levitating in the groove cut by centuries of nonstop erosion. The river flows as slowly as ever, but this morning its water is muddy, replacing its cool green hue with sickly gray.

"You will make a good teacher, Lien-Hua," he says eventually. She glances at him.

"I'm never going to be a teacher."

"You already are—you have taught me many things." He takes her hand. "You have to finish."

"No!" she cries. "No, I will not go back to Beijing."

"What about that summer program you told us about?"

"I'm not doing that either. I'm not leaving."

He sighs. For a rural man, a farmer, a villager, he has a keen understanding of the way things work.

"Lien-Hua, I don't think any of us can stay."

"What do you mean?" she asks.

"I mean, when the government arrives, I think villages like ours will be closed. You feel the ground trembling even now, as I do—this area is not safe. Our future may be elsewhere."

She blinks back tears and surveys the landscape stretching out at her feet—familiar terrain she may never see again.

"Well, wherever you and mother go, I will go also. I do not want to return to school. I do not want to work with children—"

Her voice fades and she covers her face.

"Daughter, it was not your fault."

She shakes her head, weeping uncontrollably.

"It was not your fault," he repeats, pulling her close. She convulses, pounds on his chest. Her voice rises into the cool air, the bitter sounds of grief piercing the stillness. Eventually her sobbing recedes into a gentle cry, and her father does what he can to soothe her. "Nothing you could do," he hums. "Nothing you could do."

By now the sun has found its way out of the canyon and is warming the east-facing slopes. Lien-Hua's father is weary, but he will not leave without persuading her that the measure of recovery is how thoroughly one gets back to life.

"You once told me children were the most important people," he tells her, recalling a similar morning years earlier. "You were only four years old then, and I considered it the pride of a child that made you say it. But I realize now that you have always loved children. And you know what else I've realized?"

She raises her tear-streaked face.

"You were right."

They sit for several more wordless minutes.

"Daughter, if you help a child—especially a child in pain—that is significant. You have that opportunity, don't waste it. I want you to go to this camp for orphans, and then decide whether or not to go back to school. Consider it the silly request of an old man: Go to Nanchang, and decide there how you want to spend your life."

"I don't know if I can," she replies. "I'm afraid."

"Listen to me, Lien-Hua. You saved that girl." She looks confused, skeptical. "I mean it, you saved her life. When you see her family's neighborhood, you will understand. If she had been at home, she would have died. It is still tragic. I am distraught, as you are. But she is alive because of you. Do not be afraid of helping children—you are off to a good start."

"But how?" she asks. "Camp is in a little more than a month, and we are stuck here. How will I leave you and mother and travel to Nanchang?"

"I will help you," he answers quickly. "Say the word."

Together, the father and daughter who will soon have to leave gaze down at the river that will always be there, at the mountains and plateaus shuffled across the countryside, at endless green farms and bamboo hamlets. It is all changed, if imperceptibly. Less innocent. Less intact.

Lien-Hua nods her agreement. Love would be the only way out of this.

Becomes the unspoken

It's a warm morning, and Silas shifts his weight awkwardly from foot to foot as he stands next to a young Chinese translator he just met five minutes ago. Someone told him her name, but he's forgotten. The camera hanging around his neck is fogged up from the hot, moist air in the hotel lobby after sitting under the air conditioner in his room all night. Besides about two dozen volunteers, there are ten staff members whose job it is to keep the camp running, keep everyone fed and make it possible for the volunteers to focus on the children. The group is gathered by the front doors of the hotel, awaiting their first orphans of the summer.

All around Silas, volunteers are talking eagerly with their translators, and some have even brought small gifts to break the ice. But he can't think of anything to discuss with the petite young woman beside him. He wipes the sweat from his bald head with his palm, and a taxicab pulls up to the front steps. Out jumps Douglas, the plucky camp director, who ascends the steps three at a time and bursts through the door announcing that the orphans will arrive within five minutes. Silas turns and touches his translator's arm.

"What's your name again?" he asks. She shrugs off his hand, looking at the tiled floor.

"Lien-Hua," she says quietly.

"Leen Wa?" he asks.

"*Lee-yen Wha.*"

Silas tries a couple more times.

"I'm sorry, I'm not going to get it," he tells her, chuckling. "What does it mean?"

"Lotus flower."

"Oh, that's pretty. What does a lotus flower look like?"

"Like flower," she says curtly.

He takes the hint; camaraderie will have to wait.

"Well, can I just call you Flower?" he asks. She doesn't answer. "It would be easier for me, and that way you won't have to hear me mispronounce your name all week."

She nods and he looks back toward the entryway, a gaping set of glass doors from where hot air is pouring into the lobby. Flower steals a glance upward. She hadn't meant to seem hostile when she shrank from his touch—distant, maybe, but not hostile. Several women from her village had warned her about American men when she was leaving, and their warnings had been dormant until Silas ambled into the lobby ten minutes ago and held out the largest hand she'd ever shaken.

She is terrified of him, and more than a little worried about being part of his "family" for the week. She has likewise forgotten his name, and it takes several minutes to work up the courage to ask.

He feels a gentle tug on his sleeve.

"What is your name?" she asks. "Sorry, I've forgotten."

"Oh, that's OK," he says. "I'm Silas."

She squints. "Siross?" He throws his head back and laughs. Other translators look at him, laughing above the rest of the crowd, then at her. She blushes.

"No, no. Sigh-las," he says, emphasizing the L. "Silas."

"Sigh-ras."

"Just call me Ace," he says. "It's my nickname."

"Your name also Nick?" she asks, confused.

"No, sorry. A nickname is just a shorter name that people call their friends."

"A friendly name?" she asks. "Nickname?"

"Yes, exactly," he answers, relieved.

"Ace," she repeats. "I can say Ace."

They hear others in the crowd begin to murmur and clap excitedly. Some move closer to the door, and Flower tries to see but is limited by her height. She asks Silas what's happening. He's already watching a pair of small white buses circle the parking lot.

"I think they're here," he tells her. Children start piling out of the nearest vehicle.

Several of the girls run up the steps toward the lobby, and Silas spots Mel for the first time, standing opposite him by the door. She has been here for a week already, but was gone when Silas arrived last night. All of a sudden, she shouts out a name and dashes forward, embracing one of the orphan girls. Douglas appears next to Silas, answering his unspoken question.

"We had a lot of these kiddos at last year's camp, so some of them know us," he explains in a light Aussie accent. "They're a rowdy bunch, these little ankle biters. But they're good at heart. Love 'em and they'll treat ya right, y'know?"

Not awaiting a response, Douglas weaves his way to the front and greets the children with smiles and pats on the head. Then he consults his clipboard and begins reading names. Some Americans are paired with two children, some with one. Halfway down the list is a young man from the heartland of America, thousands of miles from home and even further away culturally.

"Silas King and Lien-Hua," Douglas says, locking eyes with the burly volunteer. "Here's your lad." He bends down and says a few words to an orphan at his elbow, pointing at Silas and prodding him in that direction. The boy sidles toward Flower, who is holding out a hand invitingly. He keeps an eye on Silas as he approaches, moving as one would to cross the street in front of a semi truck.

Like most of the other orphans, he is wearing a small, half - full backpack containing a change of clothes and a stuffed animal— all his worldly possessions, and still more than some of the children. A few are without backpacks, clutching only toothbrushes or cheap water bottles as they walk in, looking bewildered.

Flower is smiling, trying hard to elicit warmth from the boy, who is too intimidated by Silas to notice. She laughs nervously and tells him the child is scared of him, so he crouches and extends his hand. The boy doesn't understand; he looks up at Flower and she says a few words in Mandarin. He reaches out and grabs Silas' pinky, unsure of what happens next. Silas laughs yet again and asks what his name is. Flower relays and the boy answers quietly.

"He says his name is Junjie."

"Junjie?" Silas asks. "Well, at least I can say that one, but I don't know if I'll remember it. Ask if I can call him Jerry."

She does, and the boy nods, still clutching Silas' finger.

"Jerry it is," he says, slapping his knee. "How old are you?"

The answer comes back eleven. And yes, he is hungry. Just then, Douglas reaches the end of the roster and announces that it's time to walk to lunch, which is served in a small family restaurant down a narrow country road. The walk takes eight to fifteen minutes, depending on who's walking, and the heat is almost enough to turn back the weak-hearted.

A few hundred yards into the sweltering midday sun, Silas offers to let Jerry ride on his shoulders. Flower translates while he smiles down at the boy. Jerry, however, doesn't smile. He just shakes his head and steps silently down the road. Silas understands children, and knows it will take time for Jerry to warm up to him. He is cheerful and jokes with the other volunteers as they walk. Several of the teenage boys from the U. S. have already quizzed Silas on his height and other physical statistics, openly envying his stature.

Silas is glad to see the first family group turn off the road toward a three-story building in the middle of a field. Several dogs lounge on the steps, and inside a husband and wife have arranged half a dozen round tables topped with giant lazy susans. Silas leads Flower and Jerry to a table by the window, where there is at least a slight breeze to take the edge off the uncooled dining room. Beads of sweat rise on Silas' back and forearms. Heat like this is rare even in Kentucky.

Several teenagers wait on the odd crowd, which is probably the first large group of foreigners to ever dine in the obscure little mountain restaurant. They set down steaming bowls of rice, vegetables and meat in various sauces and textures. Silas pokes skeptically at some of it and passes, spinning the food to his left. But he finds a few dishes to be very likeable and satisfying. He loads as much as will fit in his small bowl, then heaps another helping. It's not until he's on seconds—hungrier than he thought— that he notices Jerry eating frantically, as if it would be his final meal.

"Tell him to slow down," Silas says to Flower. "Tell him there's plenty of food for everyone."

She translates and the boy hardly looks up. He eats almost as much as Silas, and in less time, then sits back hard in his chair after finishing the last of the rice. Silas laughs and pats Jerry's stomach, stretched by its contents. There is a lull in conversation between tables while a few people finish eating, and Silas looks around the room, surveying faces for one in particular. He spots her against the opposite wall and leans forward for a better view.

She looks up at the least opportune moment and Silas waves pathetically, like, *Here I am. In China. Surprised?* She frowns and rolls her eyes.

A few minutes later, the slow-moving group is making its way back to the hotel. Douglas is the only one who walks like he has anywhere to go, assuming a pace that takes him from the back of the caravan to the front by the time they reach the hotel. The temperature has risen again, lifting moisture off the greenery blanketing everything in sight. If it's not grass or bamboo, it's moss on top of rocks, or algae riding a series of ponds by the road. Green everywhere. Silas doesn't notice the camp director until he's elbow-to-elbow with him.

"Watch out for mozzies at night," Douglas says seriously, sounding like a man who has every expectation of being perfectly understood. He nods for emphasis. "Suck you dry they will."

Silas knows he must be talking about some kind of undesirable creature, but which one is a mystery.

"I'm sorry, mozzies?" he asks.

"Oh yeah, mate. Mozzies. Y'know, mo-skee-toes?"

"Oh, mosquitoes! Because of the standing water, right?"

"Yeah, exactly. Those bities get to ya at night and it's all over but the singin'," Douglas says. "But don't you worry, big fella, we've put a bit o' fly wire in every room. Y'know, for the bed? And if one gets in just give it the flick. One little mozzie ain't gonna kill ya, right?"

"Um, no?" Silas answers.

"Right."

Another volunteer nearby is laughing at the exchange, and when Douglas continues forward, Silas gets her attention, mouthing a silent question.

"Fly wire?"

"Mosquito netting," she answers.

"What's 'the flick'?"

"I think he just means kill it before it bites you." She laughs again.

It seems like Douglas has a way of turning his accent off and on, using it for effect and switching it almost completely off in serious moments.

Flower and Silas walk Jerry to his room and tell him they'll return after naptime. When she turns to leave, Silas senses an opportunity. He jogs up next to her and asks if she's enjoying camp so far.

"Yes, I like camp," she answers, still walking toward the other side of the open plaza dividing the hotel.

"What do you think of Jerry?" he asks.

"Jerry is a good boy. Well-behaved. He will be fine." Her words are deliberate and choppy. The distance to the opposite block of rooms is narrowing, and Silas has one question left. He skips one pace ahead of her and turns to walk backwards.

"What do you think of me?"

She stops and glances up at him before looking away.

"I don't know," she says. "You are... large."

He nods and holds out his hands, helpless to do anything about it. "I hope you're not afraid of me," he says. "I'm a big softy."

"Softy? What is softy?"

"It means I'm harmless," he answers. "I just want to be friends."

She considers it.

"OK," she says. "I will be your friend."

"And friends know more about each other than just names."

"What do you want to know?"

"Well, where are you from?"

"Do you know where is Chengdu?"

"No."

"Sichuan Province?"

"No."

"You know earthquake? In May?"

Silas puts his hand to his forehead, struggling to remember

even one current event from outside the U.S.

"May was kind of a busy month for me," he says. "I'm sorry. Was it a big earthquake?"

Her eyes glaze over and she nods.

"How big?"

No answer. Silas notices teardrops forming in her eyes and mumbles an apology. Flower covers her face and hurries out of the courtyard.

Stunned, Silas hangs his head and starts walking to his room. The first half of his first day at camp has been uphill, a mess of confusion and unfamiliarity. He's not sure what to make of it— any of it, from the frozen little boy to the emotional translator. He's in a daze when Mel rounds a corner and they collide. She's mixing craft paint in a paper cup, and most of it splatters on his white shirt, an eclectic paste of yellow and blue.

"Oh my gosh!" she says before noticing whom she just assaulted with colors. "I'm so sorry."

"That's OK," he says. Her head shoots up.

"Oh. Silas, hi," she stammers, wiping yellow off her wrist. "Sorry about your shirt."

"No worries, I brought plenty—one for each day and then some. If I play this right, I might be able to avoid doing any laundry."

"Let me know how that works out."

They look at each other awkwardly.

"How do you like China so far?" she asks.

"It's... hot. The people are interesting—different than I expected."

"What did you expect?"

"I don't know, I guess they're not as welcoming as I thought."

"Not hitting it off with Lien-Hua?"

"Who?"

"Your translator."

"Oh, Flower," he says. "No, she doesn't like me very much. I was trying to make conversation just now, get to know her a little, and I think I hit a nerve. She ran into her room, crying."

"Nice, Silas."

"Well, I didn't know! I just asked about the earthquake and—"

"That's why," Mel interrupts. "Her family was right in the middle of it, they were relocated and she had a rough time even making it to camp."

"I wish I'd known. Honestly, I think I'm worse off now than this morning, when she was just scared of me."

"You're an intimidating guy," she says. It's a compliment and reminder of their breakup. "The new Silas is tough, manly. Is that a new tattoo?" She points at his shoulder. "Aces. Clever."

He looks at the floor and moves to go around Mel. She sidesteps into his path.

"I hope you know what you're doing here," she says. "This isn't a joke to those kids."

"I'm here, aren't I?" he answers sharply, getting his back up. "I'm trying!"

"Well, try not to upset your translator too much—she's been through a lot in the past few months. And don't make eyes at me, OK? I'm here for the children, not you."

"Likewise," he says. "Don't flatter yourself."

She rolls her eyes again as they part, and five minutes later they're in their respective rooms, thinking about the two solid years they had under their belt back in Kentucky. She feels not regret, but pain; Silas is pure regret. He cranks the wall-mounted air conditioner and falls backward onto his bed, which collapses under his weight.

Regret

Toy paint brushes are just not meant to fit Silas' big hands, he thinks to himself as an oscillating fan blows across his face. In fact, nothing about Silas lends itself to children's crafts, not even the fact that he is an older brother of six. He is used to wrestling with brothers and reading to sisters, but at home he was not asked to paint flowers in scrapbooks or weave bracelets or handle microscopic stickers, which is another thing his wide fingers were never intended to do.

There's a whole list of chores he had convinced his mother he was too large to do properly back home, such as milking the family's three goats or tending their organic garden. When he was a teenager, he would inevitably come inside with goat milk on his shirt after trampling a row of young corn and try to sneak by his mother, who had a sense about these things.

"Silas?" she'd call from the kitchen, "Are all my plants still a-live?"

"*All?*" he'd respond. Her head would appear around the corner.

"Did you milk Sassy?"

"Tried to," he'd say, shrugging. "She's scared of me."

After months of this he was relieved of garden and dairy duties. Today, sitting at the craft table, Silas wishes he could get out of a lot of things. He is doing a mediocre job of appearing happy, but quietly begins to wonder if coming to China was a mistake. Several of the female volunteers nearby are expertly applying paste, drawing perfect photo frames on blank pages and generally putting Silas to shame. He looks across the table at Jerry, whose method of scrapbooking seems to be heavily invested in stickers. His pages are covered with glittery turtles and dinosaurs, even though Flower is telling him to leave room for pictures that will be taken throughout the week.

After forty-five minutes of crafts, everyone migrates into the open air of the courtyard, where a small stage is set up to elevate musicians and actors for an hour each night. Soon a handful of young staff members are singing and doing hand motions on the stage. A girl plays guitar, another sings into a cheap microphone, and the whole ordeal is broadcast over a pair of speakers, echoing through the plaza. The children are thrilled to be singing, and when the choruses come along, they clap in time and shout what few words they recognize.

Jerry sings off-key, but earnestly, and he appears to be liking camp more and more as the day nears its end. He has even giggled once or twice when Silas tickled his side.

The music lifts Silas' spirits momentarily, but after a few songs a cast of volunteers takes the stage and performs a sketch that nails him. As the imaginary curtains part, one of the actors stands proudly on the stage, feet planted wide apart, arms crossed, with a haughty smirk on his face. Several needy people cross his path, but he wordlessly refuses to help, all but ignoring the unlucky passersby. The impression is that this is a supremely vain person, pathetic in his vanity, but respected. He is a figure of strength and stability, a man's man who commands reverence—things Silas had desired to be thought of him three years ago. And back in Lexington, he had successfully built just that reputation. But this character is also oblivious to the pain around him; he is so set on maintaining his stature that he will not descend, not for anyone.

Silas can't resist the comparison: Is that him on the stage, arms crossed to the nearby distress and squalor? He steals a glance at Melissa, remembering for the first time a few key adjectives he had written off the instant they left her mouth three years before.

Arrogant. Cavalier. Egotistic. Conceited.

He winces. She was right and it is him on the stage.

Next he takes a sweeping look at the little persons surrounding him, the small brown-skinned orphans who are riveted by the pantomime skit. His arms have been crossed toward them, as well, and the millions of others around the world who weren't worth his attention just weeks earlier.

Finally he looks at Jerry. The boy's hands are on his knees, the posture of an old man, and he is leaning this way and that for a glimpse of the action. He laughs when the other children laugh, and shouts when they shout at the players up front. He is a normal child, Silas decides. So what went wrong?

When the skit ends, Douglas carries a chair to the middle of the stage and sits in it. He has no book, no outline from which to read when he launches into a generic, but detailed, story of a knight and a princess. Silas is lost in thought, replaying his rationale—struggling, in fact, to answer the pointed question Mel had posed at church: *What are you thinking?*

Suddenly he feels a little warm hand tug softly on his arm. It's Jerry, and when he has dragged Silas' elbow out of the way he climbs into his lap, perched for a better view of the storyteller. Silas is thrilled; instantly, his distractions and regret evaporate as he shifts to better support the boy's weight. Flower notices, but doesn't react, watching out of the corner of her eye as Silas loops one of his thick arms around Jerry's torso. The boy reclines, and though he seems caught up in the story, his move into the big man's lap was not really for a better view. He has not felt an arm around him in years.

"It's not the easiest place to work," Douglas admits, scanning the roomful of weary faces. He's not talking about the hotel or the hot and humid mountains, or even China. He's talking about the children.

He has assembled the team in an air-conditioned room for the first of their nightly debriefings. They sit in a circle, sobered by a day of collisions with children whose defenses to abandonment, abuse and neglect have created thick barriers against attachment. Only a few of the volunteers feel trusted by their assigned orphans, but that's to be expected, Douglas tells them.

"These are kids who don't feel valued—maybe never have. And love?" he exclaims, scoffing. "Don't even talk o' love. They don't know it."

He scans the room again. Most people are looking at their feet, a few have Bibles out, some are listening with their eyes closed.

"So?" Douglas asks. "How'd it go today? Hot, I know—like a tin roof in Marble Bar. Ain't that right, little fella?"

He nudges Silas, who is wedged next to him on a small sofa.

"Are you trying to say it was hot today?" Silas asks.

"Yep."

"Then yes, hot as a tin roof in—where'd you say?"

"Oh, forget it."

Douglas pulls out a Bible with a worn cover. "Turn to one

Corinthians thirteen," he says. Silas folds his hands over his chest. "Don't you have a Bible there, Ace?"

"I've read it."

"Ah, but it's new every morning," Douglas says without skipping a beat. "Someone share their book with my friend here."

He reads several verses, ending on "love never fails" and pausing to let it sink in.

"I want to briefly describe what's happening inside those kids downstairs," he says. "Picture a carousel, but instead of painted ponies there are visions of abuse, cruel words, a hundred painful memories—take your pick. Round and round they go, keeping you awake at night, extinguishing every ray of hope as soon as it starts to flicker. No matter where you look, pain is staring back at you. Close your eyes if you want; instead of music there's a recording of everyone who's ever told you you're worthless. You cannot escape, you cannot make it stop, you cannot fill your mind with anything else."

Douglas pauses, scans the room.

"We are here to stop the ride for a week," he says. "And to insert a few memories of our own—good things they can look to when it all collapses in on them again.

"Love is so much more than any of us can even imagine. It is holding hands with a child whose sense of touch is distorted by years of abuse. It's a grin and a wink after a hard day. And it's making war on all that is wrong and harmful. Back home, love may come softly, but here—"

He looks around again, shaking his head and swallowing hard. "Here, it's a battle."

Douglas reads a few more verses.

"One last thing I want to say about this week: One of our primary goals is to relieve some of the bitterness these little guys are harboring. It's not right, the way it chews them up. We don't excuse or dismiss the wrongs they've endured, but we try to turn their eyes to better things, showing them they have value and a future. Showing them, not just repeating it endlessly. That's what this week is about: show them what love is."

A woman raises her hand.

"How are we supposed to show them love if they stay at arm's length all week?"

"Well, if they are, they are," he replies. "Nothin' you can necessarily do but try. But I think you'll find that if you're consistent, if you open up to them and stay open, they'll come 'round. It's only Monday, remember. We have four more days. And three until life chart night.

"On Thursday, we split up into families and have the kids chart their happiness—a mark for each year of their lives—whatever they can remember. If they put a ten, ask what was good about that year; a one, maybe coax them to tell that story, too. It's their best chance to release some of the hurt. Everything leads up to it. The whole week hinges on it."

Silas has already been trying to figure Jerry out—what had made an orphan of him? Pain was obviously there, it was in the glazed eyes and cold distance the boy kept. So Thursday night would be the only opportunity to discover it, to learn the story and perhaps undo some of the agony.

"Look," Douglas continues, "we know five days is a might short of what we'd need to fix these kids. We're not gonna fix 'em in a week, we know that. But a good first step is to help e-motionally, try to repair some of the scarring that's happened in their lives.

"If we can peel away a layer of emotional scar tissue this week, I say mission accomplished."

Silas has never been particularly fond of boiled eggs, but it's the only part of breakfast that's familiar, so he's peeled three and is putting the first one in his mouth when Flower and Jerry take seats on either side of him. Eight in the morning is early to Silas, but thanks to a lingering case of jet lag, he rose at six this morning and went for a jog. Or started to. A hundred feet out the front door, he realized the early morning air wasn't much cooler than the 90 degrees that had seen him and the others off to bed.

Flower leaves and comes back with an armful of food for the three of them, serving Jerry first, then Silas. She hands him a bag of room-temperature liquid plastered with bright labels and Chinese symbols. He asks what it is and she says milk. Eyebrows a-loft, he sets the bag aside as discreetly as possible. Next she hands him a pair of warm dumplings, and he devours the first one despite its being the blandest thing he's ever eaten. When he bites into the second one, however, he finds a clump of ground meat in the middle, grimacing when he sees that it is not fully cooked. But Flower is watching him, so he gulps down the rest of the dumpling, mystery meat and all.

"Tasty?" she asks.

"Oh, yeah," he answers, nodding profusely.

Flower giggles. "You don't like milk?"

That's where Silas draws the line. He shrugs. "I like it cold— you know, refrigerated?"

Today will be their first day at the public swimming pool down the mountain in Nanchang. Fifteen minutes after breakfast, everyone files onto a city bus with a dour-looking driver, who scrutinizes the children as they board, checking for gum.

There are fewer seats on the bus than people, and Silas stands in the aisle, grasping bars on either side of his head as the driver pulls out of the hotel parking lot and rockets down a narrow country road toward the city. Rice terraces divide the hillsides; bamboo crowds the curvy road, shoots that are thicker and taller than Silas thought was possible—some six inches in diameter, reaching higher than telephone poles.

From his place near the front of the bus, Silas feels the rush of air through a vent above him and closes his eyes as the big vehicle jolts right and left. Eventually the driver maneuvers onto a wide city street, freely using a loud horn to notify and warn anyone in his way—pedestrians, women on mopeds wearing visors over their faces, other vehicles, animals, flaggers. At one point he honks at a police car that looks like it might pull out in front of him.

Silas is fascinated with the spectacle of Chinese traffic. It's a free-for-all, drivers nosing their vehicles past others and through crowds of people at intersections. Behind, beside and around the quick-moving cars flow streams of bicyclists, who nimbly avoid being run over but regularly experience the wrath of the city's motorists. Silas gets the impression that driving in China is less about shifting and turn signals than harassment.

Eventually, the driver pulls off the boulevard and onto a small one-way side street. He squeezes past cars parked on both sides toward a driveway several hundred feet ahead. A staff member asks a translator to tell the driver that he can stop any time; they'll walk the rest of the way. But it's clearly not about getting the passengers close to their destination. He denies the request because it's about asserting the authority of his bus over this particular street and everything on it. City bus drivers, Silas would later learn, are the cream of the professional driving crop, and they know it. He would also learn that such buses are called "city boats" in China.

Minutes later, no one can deny the captain's skill as they disembark within feet of the entrance to the public pool. They step into downtown air that is thick with the same humidity as the mountains, but also carrying a variety of aromas, from fried noodles to rotting garbage. A small crowd gathers when white people start stepping into the street, and Silas earns the most attention.

People point and whisper as he walks through the gate holding Jerry's hand.

Inside, the children are handed life vests as they clamor to reach the pool.

"It's like herding cats," Silas says to Flower.

"Hurting cats?" she asks, puzzled. "Why hurting cats?"

"No, *herding*. Do you know what a herd is?"

She shakes her head.

"It's difficult," he says, pointing to the rambunctious kids.

"Oh yes, difficult," she agrees. "Very difficult."

They proceed through one last gate and place their things in a shady corner. Silas absent-mindedly peels off his shirt, revealing his several tattoos, and turns to find Flower staring at the dark patterns and images on his back.

"So many," she says.

"Yeah, that's what my mom said, too."

There's a splash nearby, and moments later Jerry bobs to the surface, face down and thrashing wildly. Silas jumps into the water beside the boy and lifts him up, gasping and frightened. Silas has to resist laughing as he sets Jerry on the concrete platform and reaches for his life vest, which is lying a few feet away, forgotten in a moment of overwhelming delight.

All around the edge of the pool, orphans who have never been swimming before are plunging in, filled with joy until they sink and come up sputtering. Once righted, the kids revel in the cool freedom of the water. There is an innocence in them that

Silas has never seen—a purity that lives parallel to the evils they've endured. To jaded Americans who have experienced every kind of thrill, seeing children so worked up about a swimming pool is not just endearing or refreshing—it's also tragic, because it belies how seldom they get to enjoy being kids.

As he untangles the strap of Jerry's life vest and loops it around his chest, he sees in the boy's eyes an urgency to take it all in—the pool, the city, the heaps of food they are served at every meal, the singing, the quality time. He is frantic to get in the pool, not only because it looks like fun, but because he wants to live as much of his paused childhood as he can in these five days.

Flower tells Jerry that the vest will keep him afloat until he learns how to swim, and then Silas wades around the massive, chest-deep pool with the orphan in his arms, acclimating him to the water and demonstrating how to stay right side up. Jerry grips tightly for several minutes while his courage returns, and Silas has just noticed Mel at the far end of the pool when Jerry splashes his face, setting off the first of many water wars the man and his boy will have this week.

Silas instantly forgets about Mel, but she watches him for several minutes as she begins to question her assumptions. She is still not convinced, still skeptical that his smiles could be part of an elaborate performance. But for the first time in years, she feels like she's watching the true Silas—not the imposter from Lexington—as he fends off hoards of boys who pile on top of him in a boyish challenge of manly strength. With three or four hanging off his arms and neck, he'll let himself be pulled under, then emerge and toss one high into the air. Before long, he is the engine pulling a train of children around the pool, each hanging on to the shoulders in front of them.

After an hour and a half of swimming, Silas exits and notices the air temperature has risen at least ten degrees. The sun is blaring into the pool area, which had previously been shadowed by tall apartment buildings on three sides. The water is murky, a dubious brew of additives he would rather avoid listing. Instead, he sits on the edge of the pool, feet in the water and hands resting on concrete. Flower sees him from across the pool and thinks he looks like a professional wrestler, all tattoos and bald head and muscular shoulders. Jerry sees him and thinks he looks like a superhero.

But Silas is suffering inside, observing the kids and other volunteers—ordinary people, like him, who unlike him had saved hard-earned money to come to China with pure motives. He had chased an ex-girlfriend here, hoping in the meantime to impress his father into paying for one more year of school. Is it just an act, then? Is he just playing a role?

Impressive though he may appear, perched like a statue, he feels like a fool. Pathetic at heart, nothing to offer. Sweat slides to the tip of his nose and down the inside of his arms. The vivid sights and scents of downtown Nanchang grow distant to him. He wishes he could get out.

Suddenly there is a pattering of small feet behind him. Jerry sits down next to Silas, having ditched his life vest, and slides toward him, as close as he can get. He grins and looks Silas up and down, placing his own little hands on the edge of the pool like Silas. Straightening his back like Silas. Jutting his junior chest out past his arms like Silas.

And there they sit, one smiling, satisfied with his imitation; one trying to conceal his sobs. The only two people to notice are both young women, who see his giant shoulders trembling and turn away to hide their own tears.

A boy handling treasure

Silas hasn't cried since he was thirteen, and only then because his soccer team made it all the way through the playoffs and lost by a penalty kick in overtime. Under any other circumstances, embarrassment would be his natural reaction. "Crying in public," he snorts to himself as he lies down for a nap on the second day of camp. "What's happening to me?"

The question is beyond rhetorical: Not only does he know what's happening, he wants it to happen. Thirty seconds beside the pool this morning were all it took to strip what was left of his fa-cade. Here was a boy who openly admired him, and for once the admiration was meaningful—not hollow, like when guys would fold a hand of cards and surrender their money wishing they could play like that.

This is different. This is real life, truly high stakes—a chance to matter. He drifts to sleep with a heart condition he never could have anticipated and an orphan on his mind.

It's not that crafts are more enjoyable on Tuesday than they were on Monday, but this time Silas is focused. He blitzes the craft room wearing a sweat band, ready to work. He spins a chair under him, winking at Jerry and collecting oversized markers in various colors. He asks Flower to draw the Chinese symbols for her name, then Jerry's name, then he copies the lines onto one of the pages in the boy's memory book. Flower adds a third set.

"What's that say?" he asks.

"It means Ace," she replies, adding a few last curves and dashes to the characters. "Your nickname," she adds, proud to have remembered.

The three of them have their picture taken, and this time Silas remembers not to put his arm around Flower. After pasting the Polaroid in Jerry's memory book, they head around the back of the hotel, to an abandoned basketball court where Douglas has set up an inflatable water slide and several ankle-deep pools with water guns and buckets. Jerry and Silas launch a squirt gun assault against all of the girls—Flower is noticeably absent—then take over the water slide.

With the largest, strongest person at his back, Jerry is all bravado—the very picture of confidence. He plays king of the water slide with Silas as his enforcer, only letting certain people through. Several of the teenage Americans try to tackle Silas, but he easily tosses them head over heels down the slide. Eventually, all the boys team up and dislodge Silas and Jerry in a tangle of arms and feet, emptying the small pool at the bottom.

Forty-five minutes whistle by and the group begins migrating back toward the front of the hotel. As they walk, Silas feels something sharp wedged into the waistband of his trunks. He fishes it out and holds up a tooth, clean and white. His first reaction is alarm, until he realizes that most of the children are around the age when baby teeth are falling out. He laughs and wonders whose it might be, looking at all the little faces. The last child he checks is Jerry, who is smiling up at him with a gaping hole just behind his left lower canine.

Inside the hotel, musicians are warming up as Silas takes a detour to the craft room, pulling Jerry along quickly. The boy sits at one of the marker-stained tables while Silas fishes out his memory book and a roll of tape. Flipping to a blank page, Silas tapes down the tooth and snaps a self-portrait of the two of them.

As he waves the paper square back and forth, he watches Jerry flip through the book. Its thick pages are warped with finger paint and paste and stickers, but the look in his eyes is one of a boy handling treasure. He is memorizing the smiles, the scenery and atmosphere of camp, lingering on every picture. Where Silas and Flower have drawn or written, Jerry traces the lines with his fingertips. Silas knows the book will be an important record of good memories when the orphanage takes the boy back and immerses him in reminders of pain. He glues the toothless grin beside the boy's molar and they walk toward the singing out in the courtyard.

As they approach the stage, Silas notices one of the male translators talking to Flower. Silas recognizes him—he's a smallish guy with a good sense of humor and a penchant for saying outrageous things in the most innocent way.

Flower and the young man, who has adopted the English name Theodore—insisting against the shorter "Ted" or "Theo" — stand to the side while Silas and Jerry walk into a row of seats. Silas wants to find out whether they're just deep in conversation or flirting, so when the pair sits down beside Jerry, he counts to ten and moves back two rows. Flower and Theodore are oblivious; they remain in their seats and lean toward each other to whisper nothing in particular.

Silas shakes his head knowingly.

"That's what I thought," he says to the boy, who just looks at him. Silas points a thumb in their direction, then folds his hands under his cheek and bats his eyelashes. "They're flirting." Jerry understands and laughs, mimicking Silas' sign language for lovestruck teenagers.

After music and a skit, Silas walks Jerry to his room before the nightly volunteer meeting upstairs. He and Flower are standing in the doorway when Jerry turns and says something to her.

She leans against the wall and hesitates, looking at Silas. Her expression says this is an important question; Silas gets the message and nods.

"He wants to know if you think he can be big and strong like you someday," she tells Silas.

He knows he'll be late to the meeting, but it doesn't matter. He sits down on the bed and motions for the boy to stand in front of him, then raises his right arm, flexing and pointing at Jerry's arm. He raises it like Silas and flexes as hard as he can, mustering a slight bump of a bicep. Silas grunts his approval, then repeats with the other arm. Next he turns Jerry away from him and holds both his arms up. Jerry understands and flexes his little back.

"Tell him I think he will be a strong man," he tells Flower. "And tell him something I've learned this week is that strength lives here," he taps the boy's head, "and here." He places a hand on Jerry's chest, and when Flower is done translating pulls him in for a hug.

Silas says goodnight and bounds up the stairs. Flower closes the door to Jerry's room and walks halfway across the courtyard, taking a seat in the dim, warm night air. She thinks about her parents, who are in a government camp twenty miles from their village. And she thinks about the village, wondering if she'll see it again. She remembers leaving the paralyzed girl with her parents, who had been talking of adoption when they put Flower on the train for Nanchang. Crying softly, she finally recalls the boy whose body had been extracted after several days by local men working tirelessly to save or bury their own before government help arrived.

When thoughts of home have run their course, Flower turns her attention to Silas, who has changed even in the two days they've spent together as a family. She had been skeptical of his a-bility to relate to a little Chinese orphan, but as it turns out, he didn't have to relate. All he had to do was reach for the boy; Jer-ry, it seemed, was just waiting to be reached for. They are per-fect together, she thinks.

Upstairs, Silas enters a meeting in progress as quietly as possi-ble, taking the only space available: a seat on the floor next to Melissa. He doesn't notice her hair is pulled back in pigtails—his favorite—or that her body language shifts when he sits down. Af-ter the pool, she spent all day watching the transformation of Si-las, knowing exactly what was happening. In previous years as a camp counselor, she'd seen the same signs in almost everyone, in-cluding herself. She knows the power of love to strip away false selves and align priorities. She only wishes she could share this ex-perience with the man seated beside her.

Douglas is answering a question about what will happen to the older orphans, and Silas is immediately caught up in the discussion. He hasn't given much thought to Jerry's future, and what the camp director has to say hits home.

"Fourteen is the magic number if you want to be adopted," Douglas says. "Most of them get jobs, some end up on the

streets, and the rest go into adoption or some other living ar-
rangement."

Silas asks how an orphan would choose a career.

"Basically, they line you up and say, 'Congratulations, you're
going to be a welder.' And you go to welding school and you
weld until you die.

"The future is an entirely different concept for these kids than
it was for us when we were young," he adds. "When folks asked
what we wanted to do when we grew up, we had to sort through
a list of options—doctor, teacher, architect, athlete. All within
reach. Ask any one of these orphans, and they'll either recite a
fantasy or ask you to explain what you mean. No one's told them
they can choose, no one says they can achieve. All signs point to
failure and obscurity, so they don't even bother looking to the horizon."

For the second night in a row, the volunteers are subdued, a
result of oppressive heat and the emotional heaviness of the children they've been tasked with loving. Breakthroughs have oc-
curred for a lucky few; most are still waiting to connect. Inner
defenses have been years in the making, Douglas explains, and
they're not easy to topple in five days.

"These kids are battlers, the lot of them," he says. "They've
been through the tumbler, been hit by their folks, seen things
that are tough even for adults to bear.

"There are success stories," he adds. "I just read the other
day about a bloke who started out an orphan, went to work in a

vacuum cleaner factory, and now he owns the biggest manufactur-
er of vacuum cleaners in all of China.

"But make no mistake: It's going to be a tough go for most of
these little ones," he concludes. "They need to see a future with
more than pain in it. They need to know they'll be strong men
and smashing beautiful women, worth loving, worth fearing. They
need to be noticed, to be hugged. For Pete's sake, hug 'em every
chance you get, because the chances they get are few and fleet-
ing."

Two hours later, Silas is deep into a dream about Kentucky
when he is awakened by urgent knocking. He stumbles into a pair
of gym shorts, fumbles toward the door and opens it to find
Douglas frowning down at Jerry. Douglas prods the boy inside,
and they all sit—Silas and Jerry on the bed, Douglas in a chair a-
gainst the wall.

"Heard him in the courtyard," Douglas says as the men try to
shake off sleep. There is no anger in his voice, not even mild annoyance. He knows the kids hate sleeping at camp, terrified at the
thought of missing even the slightest moment that can be sculpted
into a memory and packed away for the orphanage. He was not
surprised to find Jerry up on the stage, pretending to be a rock
star. But he knew the boy needed sleep, and his sense of orphans
says there may be something deeper at play. He tells Silas he has
roused one of the older translators, Rodger, who arrives a few
minutes later and kneels on the floor next to Jerry.

Douglas greets the discerning translator whose superior English skills and sharp mind have made him the unofficial second- in-command in Nanchang. He nods, looking concerned, and asks what happened.

"Well, first off, tell him he's not in trouble," Douglas says. Rodger translates, and Jerry's rigid posture eases. "I just don't want him running around outside his room at night—for his safety and my peace of mind. Don't tell him that last part, about my peace of mind."

Once Douglas has reinforced the rules about staying in bed, he sits back in his chair and takes a long, searching look at the boy. Silas scoots closer to Jerry on the bed and squeezes his bony torso.

"Sometimes I can't sleep," Douglas says, almost to himself, "because there are bad things going through my mind. Tell him that, Rodger. Ask him if there's anything on his mind that's spoiling his sleep."

Jerry listens to the translation, then looks down at his knees, then back up at Rodger. His voice is quiet as he unfolds his explanation. At one point, he pats Silas on the cheek. Rodger translates for the men.

"He says he was dreaming the best dream he can remember. He was in America, and no matter where he went, he could always feel someone who loved him watching—he says it must have been Silas. He was just starting to believe it wasn't a dream when he woke up."

As Jerry continues, it's clear he is upset. His expression changes sharply and his voice rises. Rodger translates sentence by sentence, as the boy's angry words arrive.

"The first thing he saw was his father's face."

Another few words, another decibel louder.

"Then he heard his father's voice, and his dream was gone. Rotten memories were all around him."

One last phrase and Jerry collapses into tears, repeating the words over and over, rhythmic and low. Rodger looks down at his hands. He's heard it too often.

"He says, *I hate him, I hate him, I hate him.*"

Douglas and Silas have the same look in their eyes, but one of the men knows it's time to leave. His intuition proven correct, Douglas rises and squeezes Silas' arm.

"You've got this, mate," he says. The camp director exits and the door closes behind him. He turns in the warmth of the open -air hallway, rests his forehead against the door and prays.

From his place on the disheveled mattress, Silas looks at Rodger and recalls all of the pain in his life—the real pain, relatives dying and friends turning their backs on him and his own father's criticism.

"Ask him if he wants to talk about what he saw," he tells Rodger.

The answer comes back the same.

I hate him.

Silas remembers one of Douglas' talks, the one about bitterness and how toxic it is.

"Tell Jerry I don't know what his father did to him to hurt

him so badly," he says. "But I know what it's like to carry around
anger and pain. Tell him he doesn't have to carry his father's burden any more. Tell him that."

Jerry listens and sits idly for several minutes before murmu-
ring his answer.

"He says he doesn't want to, that he is looking for a way to
put it down," Rodger says.

Silas pulls the boy closer.

"I know someone who works miracles with burdens," he says
softly, "and he'll be here even after I have to go home."

———————————

Just before lunch the next day, half of the people on the bus
are asleep on the ride home from the pool. Silas resists, prefer-
ring to savor it all—the rush of air over his face, the driver still
audibly assaulting anyone who dares take up road in front of him,
the limp boy in his arms.

Jerry had climbed into his lap for a better view of the city
blocks flicking by like pages in a massive, dirty, enthralling book.
It was a volume unlike any Silas or the boy had ever experienced,
this strange, hot city. So they had watched together until Jerry
leaned his head back on Silas and slept.

For the first time, Silas is suddenly aware of Friday. It's when
goodbye letters will be unfolded and read, when the orphans will
eat with their families for the last time, and when they will climb
back onto the buses that had brought them in and "shove off," as
Douglas would say. Any headway and all opportunities for love

would end abruptly on Friday; his bond with Jerry would be frozen in time, painfully transitioned from a living experience into a memory.

Silas closes his eyes and leans into the breeze. Jerry shifts drowsily. The driver honks at a flock of sheep on the mountain road. These are thirty minutes that will never be forgotten: Bliss. Perfection.

Two rows behind them, Flower is also awake, also savoring the ride. Another orphan, a girl, has fallen asleep on her shoulder, and as she watches Silas cradle Jerry she realizes her thoughts of home have been less frequent as the week went on. And less acute. A few pleasant memories have broken through, interrupting the vicious sights and sounds that were looping through her mind during the weeks before camp.

She thinks about the day she left for Beijing to begin her freshman year. Her favorite child in the village, the boy who would die years later in her family's farm shed, came running up the road as she was walking with her father out of town. Clutching a blossom and a kite, he first held up the humble flower, freshly picked.

"Lotus flower, like your name," he had said, giggling. "Pretty like you."

Then he extended the paper kite.

"Will you fly this for me in Tiananmen?" he asked.

She had promised she would, and she did—on her second day in the capital.

After the earthquake, her father had been wise to push her toward Nanchang and the orphans. She recognized what he must have seen on that hilltop after a lucky sunrise, that love was the only therapy—not receiving it so much as channeling it to those who need it most. She has never felt as patriotic as when she is facilitating a tender moment between her giant American partner and the boy whose pain, she imagines, out-hurts her own.

As she watches Silas hold the sleeping boy, she realizes that if Jerry had grown up in her village, he would have been friends with the young admirer who'd met her on the road with such a sweet farewell years before. Jerry's sense of humor was almost identical, his crooked smile deeply familiar.

Three days, she marvels. Three days to love a boy, and in that love to heal. And in that healing, to make an all-important decision: She would return to her university in the fall. Rebuild when she could, teach when time allowed, and finish. That is what matters, that is how she can honor the one who died at her heels. A teardrop slips to her chin.

The best dream

Hoisted above the countryside, Jerry is banging out a rhythm on the skin of Silas' bald head. They are on their way to lunch, and the three of them are ahead of everyone else, thanks to the nutritional requirements of a young man from the heartland of America. Both his appetite and reputation precede him, and the family tending the restaurant point him toward a table laden with extra rice and entrees.

To Silas, the food is passable—some dishes are good, some questionable—but to Jerry, every meal is a feast. Compared with rice porridge, the pork and vegetables and watermelon heaped up at lunch and dinner time is food that orphans dream of eating. They often talk about how some of their foreign counselors can let so much fine cuisine go to waste, leaving plates half full at every meal, and Jerry likes to finish what Silas doesn't. He crams until it hurts every time.

When they sit down for lunch today, Jerry sends his chopsticks flying across bowls and platters, while Silas quizzes Douglas about Australia.

"So, are kangaroos friendly at all?" he begins. "Like, do people keep them as pets?"

Douglas tries not to cough up a mouthful of rice.

"Roos?" he asks mockingly. "I'm sorry, are we talking about those shonky critters 'at carry their young around in pouches and jump real high?"

It's not the first time Silas has felt culturally ignorant this week.

"So... they're not?" he asks.

"No, mate! In fact, they'll as soon kick ya in the noggin' as let you pet 'em. Haven't you ever watched television?"

Silas takes a few more bites of rice. He's down, but not defeated. All the foreigners at the table—two Americans and three Australians—have laid their chopsticks down and are listening to the banter.

"How did you guys come up with your language?" he asks.

"What language?" Douglas says. "We're both speaking English, right?"

"Are we?" Silas teases. "I mean, I get to China expecting to have to learn a little Chinese, but I had no idea I had to learn Australian, too."

"OK, wise guy. Spout me some Australian, then."

Silas tries pathetically to recall all the Outback slang and jargon he's ever heard. It ends poorly, and Douglas pats him on the shoulder on his way out.

"At's all right, mate. You gave it a go, anyway."

Silas has been considering a practical joke for the camp director, but couldn't decide whether he should. Now he has the motivation and the liberty, so back at the hotel he reserves the only computer with Internet access and begins researching Australia—everything from slang to wildlife to geography and national holidays. In half an hour, he knows more about the land down under than any other foreign country—and he has a strategy for getting back at Douglas.

He is about to log off when Flower enters the room.

"Hi Ace," she says. "I only need to email my father—well, not father, but friend who will tell father."

"Tell him what?" Silas asks casually.

"That I am going back to Beijing this fall."

"For school?"

"Yes, my second year in university."

"What are you studying there?"

"To be a teacher," she answers.

"Well," he says, folding the paper that holds his Australian trivia, "I think you'll be a terrific teacher. You've already taught me a lot."

Quiet descends on the hotel, its rooms and broad courtyard. Cicadas buzz outside, motorcycles pass on the road every few minutes, and Mel can't sleep. She takes a cheap fan and her Bible into the courtyard, takes a seat, flips the book open aimlessly. She can't get started, though—too much is weighing on her mind, like a conversation with Rodger over lunch.

"Melissa," he had said, "why did you come to China?"

It was *the* question.

"Have you ever heard of the Bible?" she began.

"Yes," he nodded. "Adam, Abraham, God. I have heard."

"Well, I believe everything the Bible says. And one thing it says is to spend time with orphans and widows, to help them. That's why I am here."

Mel recognized the puzzled look on his face as the beginning of a dialogue that would last beyond lunch, after the four weeks of camp had passed and questions about God would have to be answered via e-mail. Dozens of translators from previous years were already e-mailing other staff members with intelligent, sometimes pointed, questions about origins and manuscripts and meaning.

"You believe… everything?" he asked.

"Yes, everything. Every word."

"You believe there is God?"

"Yes."

Rodger sat back in his chair, stunned.

"I have never met anyone who believe there is God."

"Well, now you have," she responded warmly. "Is it so hard to believe?"

"Yes," he said. "Science is better."

"I understand why many people think science has replaced God, but I believe science can only discover some of God's ideas. Our world would be hell without some of the things in the Bible that aren't scientific."

"Like what?" he asked skeptically.

"Let's see," she had answered, sorting her thoughts. She scanned the room, full of unwanted children, castaways, second -rate people with disabilities and disadvantages. "Well, one of God's most important ideas is to take care of the poor, the sick, and the unloved—people science tells us should go away to make our species stronger. Science doesn't care about orphans."

They had talked for half an hour, and as she sits in the afternoon humidity, Mel replays every word in her mind, wondering if she was humble enough, logical enough. It felt good to be challenged by someone who was, perhaps, more intelligent than her, with a better mind for theory. Her head is bowed when Theodore approaches and sits next to her.

"I have question," announces the plucky young Chinese man. Mel looks up and shrugs, knowing this conversation will be more amusing and less intense than the one she had with Rodger.

"Hit me," she answers.

Theodore's double take is instant, dramatic.

"No!" He is scandalized. "I would never hit beautiful woman."

"No, no, it's an expression," she laughs. "It means, like, shoot."

"Shoot is worse than hit! Why this violence?"

"What I mean is, ask me your question. I am ready to answer."

He has to collect his thoughts.

"OK, my question is, what is difference between flirting and friendship?"

His look is so earnest that she has to resist the dozens of ways that come to mind to tease him. She is about to answer when he follows up with part two.

"Have you ever flirted?"

Now her thoughts are headed down an entirely different path, one lined with memories of Silas.

"Oh yes, I have flirted before," she answers. "You know Silas? Ace?" He nods eagerly, leaning forward as if hearing gossip for the first time. "He was my boyfriend for two years."

His eyebrows shoot up.

"Your boyfriend?!" he exclaims breathlessly. "He is so big!"

"What about you, Theodore, have you ever flirted with anybody?"

The cheerful young Chinese man was unprepared for a turning of the tables. He sits back in his chair, blindsided, tapping his chin. He starts to talk several times but halts, sorting through memorable encounters with the opposite sex. They are few because of the Chinese customs against contact between boys and girls at school—academics have always been too important for Theodore to pursue girls. Until a few days ago.

"No, I think I have never flirted," he decides finally. She knows better.

"What about last night out on the front steps of the hotel?" she presses.

"Oh!" he says, agonized, exposed. "Oh! How did you know that?"

"Does her name start with an *F?*"

"Oh, no! How?!"

"Theodore, were you flirting with her?" she asks accusingly.

"No!" he insists. "No, we were not flirting—just looking!"

He asks a few more questions about girls, revealing keen insight at times, and complete ignorance at others. He knows what a relationship takes, but nothing of how women think and operate. She likes Theodore, so she gives him good advice—things women usually prefer men to have to figure out for themselves. She fears he may never learn if not from her, so she starts by explaining how to flirt effectively—equal parts restraint, humor and well-timed attention—and ends at gift-giving. He leaves convinced that wooing women is too complicated for any man to ever completely succeed.

Theodore is a few steps from the stairs when Flower rounds the corner. She stops. He stops. An awkward moment passes. Theodore looks over his shoulder at Mel, who is trying not to laugh, then at the tile below his would-be girlfriend, wondering if it's time for restraint or attention. *Nice shoes,* he thinks.

Before he figures out what to say, or even looks up, Flower asks in Chinese if he would like to chat again tonight, inviting him to the steps with a coy grin. He nods his acceptance, still dumbstruck, and as she disappears on the other side of the courtyard he runs back and kneels beside Mel.

"It works!" he says. "I need you teach me more!"

"Maybe I will," she says, laughing. "We'll see."

When Theodore is gone, Mel relaxes in the hot afternoon— it's the key to enjoying a summer day in Nanchang, she's learned. Relax and keep still. Silas never was very good at the gift-giving, but boy, could he flirt. It comes naturally to a guy with such a sharp sense of humor and firm grasp on human nature.

She recalls the hot summer afternoon when Silas walked the four miles to her house just to leave a four-word sticky note on her window. He knew she was halfway through one of her ubiquitous to-do lists, which kept her organized on Saturdays full of organic gardening and chores. So he had trekked across town to add his own item to the list:

☑   *Movie tonight with Silas*

The first year and a half of their relationship was full of similar moments— "endearing" and "unique" were two words she had used to describe even routine days with Silas. Then it changed—maybe familiarity had bred contempt. She didn't know exactly how it had happened, but little things they'd sworn to ignore got heavy. It was like they were carrying their love in a wheelbarrow, and she broke it off when he started losing interest, first year of college—no coincidence.

But now, in China, he's suddenly different. Many of the qualities she once loved about him, then counted lost to his destructive ego, are resurfacing. Three days is so quick, changes are so easy to undo once home and old habits overcome the best intentions.

Still, she thinks, the fact that he has not shown any interest in her all week is a good sign. Even though she told him to stay away, she wonders why he has, why she hasn't caught him looking, even once. There have been no advances for her to rebuff, no attention whatsoever, just cordial greetings in the hallway and brief, distracted conversations—all initiated by her.

The afternoon passes around her as she reminisces and begins feeling a familiar tug inside. She knows summer camp is a lousy place to rekindle a romance, and isn't sure if Silas would even be interested. But her pulse quickens when he walks through the courtyard on his way to Jerry's room. Seated near a corner of the plaza, she wants to stop him, to spend a few minutes talking with the man behind some of her sweetest memories. She sits up, slips her feet into her sandals, but her hesitation has cost her and he reaches the opposite bank of rooms before she can get his attention.

Activities that are now routine proceed accordingly, swimming and then lunch, crafts blending into music, then another character sketch, another bedtime. Before the kids are sent off to their rooms for the night, Silas has requested five minutes on the stage. Douglas was skeptical. It was out of the ordinary, but Silas insisted on telling the bedtime story tonight, so the request was granted.

After the final song, Silas walks to the front of the audience with a small piece of paper in his hand and sits on the edge of the stage. Feet dangling in the air, he surveys the crowd, making sure the camp director is within earshot. Rodger is standing a few feet away to translate, and Silas begins.

"Once upon a time," he says, taking a deep breath to calm his racing pulse, "there was a poor man who lived in Australia."

Across the dim courtyard, Silas can see Douglas' eyebrows shoot up. His arms are crossed and he tilts his head to the side.

"He might have been poor, but this man was very handsome and very funny—the funniest man in all of Australia," Silas says. "And he could speak Australian better than anyone else in the world."

Now Douglas knows the story is aimed at him. Volunteers are chuckling and looking around for the camp director to gauge his reaction. Seated on the stage, Silas tries to keep a straight face.

"He didn't have a wife, so one day he went out looking for a woman—a beautiful, intelligent woman—to marry. The first one he found was gorgeous, but couldn't speak Australian, so she didn't laugh at any of his jokes. This made him very sad, so he kept looking.

"The second one he found was very intelligent and got his jokes, but she was not as beautiful as he would like. She was too thin, and not long after they met, a bunch of *mozzies*"—he tilts the word, straining for a believable accent— "carried her away, never to be seen again.

"Well, this poor man was starting to get old, so he told himself, 'I'd better hurry or I'll never find a wife.' The third woman he met was perfect—beautiful and smart and wealthy—but she hated him. She would only laugh at some of his jokes. One day, a kangaroo broke into her house, kicked her in the noggin and carried her off to the top of Ayers Rock, a huge stone mountain in the middle of Australia, so big it takes you a day to walk all the way around it.

"Now, this poor man thought to himself, 'Now's my chance! If I rescue her, maybe she will marry me.' So he climbed to the top of the rock, found the kangaroo and made it his pet, then set the lady free. He asked if she would marry him, but she said no. She said, 'I wouldn't marry you for all the tea in China.'

"And that's where the man is today, in China, still searching for a wife. And very few people get his jokes."

The children are puzzled, but the adults are all laughing as Douglas makes his way to the front. He grins as he approaches Silas, then turns to face the crowd.

"All right, all right, time for bed," says Douglas. "Maybe tomorrow I'll tell you the story about an ogre who leaves the Midwest for the first time."

He turns and jabs Silas on the arm.

"Well done, mate," he says. "Well done."

The volunteers are assembled again in the small, air-conditioned room buzzing with predictions about how Douglas would
get back at Silas. The two men enter together, still laughing and
cracking jokes, but within a few minutes the mood is changing
while everyone settles into their seats. After a brief prayer, the
room is still and sober as Douglas gives advice to those who need
it, speaks encouragement where he can and answers questions that
are increasingly urgent with the end of the week drawing near.
They talk about grief, scars, defenses. About why many of the
kids prefer mischief to affection.

"Pain, I think, plays tricks on the mind, and what I've seen
from a lot of orphans is that they like to manipulate situations to
keep their world the same. That's the key—familiarity: If someone
is standing in a hall of all the universe's miseries and asked to
choose one, they're inevitably going to choose the one they know,
because at least it's familiar. These kids are so sad that they would
rather just be sad than have to explore being happy."

Douglas sets his Bible aside, leans forward and scans the room,
making eye contact with each person. A few of the women are

crying—some of their girls have already unburdened their stories, describing fierce abuse and neglect. It feels too thick and unyielding to even chip away little pieces of the agony. No one has made the impact they had intended—at least not visibly. They are overwhelmed by the collective pain of such complicated, grown-up children.

"I want you to know that what you've done here this week matters. It matters eternally, and it should matter to you personally. You are heroes. If you want proof, just look—I mean really *look* —into their eyes. They know they what they mean to you. They know."

Douglas closes by reading a prayer out of Psalms, then departs. Most of the volunteers follow, ready to be alone after a long day and the most serious meeting yet. But a dozen people remain in the room, hoping to lighten the atmosphere. Someone suggests cards, and before long they are dealt. Texas hold 'em. Silas is handed a pair of eights while he is still lost in thought, but is jolted into the game when two of the teenage guys start debating who has the big blind.

"Wait, what are we playing?" Silas asks.

"Poker," several people answer in unison.

He shakes his head and tosses his pair on the carpet. "No, I can't play."

"You don't know how to play poker?" one of the boys asks, astounded.

"I mean I don't want to," he says. "I'm a different person

when I play cards."

Mel pats his shoulder.

"Oh, c'mon Ace," she says.

"Don't call me that."

"Why not? It's your nickname, right?"

"It was."

"And didn't it refer to your poker skills?"

He looks at her squarely for the first time all week. He is pained, ashamed.

"They call me Ace in Lexington," he says slowly, "because I'm the best on campus. But also because they think I'm some kind of player, a man's man who drinks hard and has all the women he wants. That reputation is something I'd rather not bring here."

It's quiet in the room. There is no awkwardness in his confession, not among comrades who have been through what they have. They understand—they've all been similarly changed, if in smaller increments.

He feels a familiar hand on his knee, then her forehead on his arm.

"That's not Silas," Mel says. "That's not you."

He closes his eyes. Douglas has been talking about grace, but Silas never knew quite what it felt like until now. Wordlessly, he picks up his cards.

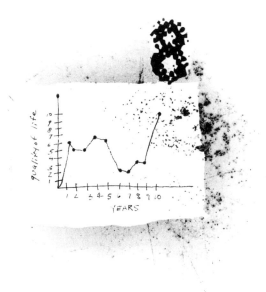

Eights and nines

Too soon the last night descends, and with the change from bright to dim outside, Jerry's demeanor shifts. It is subtle, like a screen door slid over his thoughts and feelings, obscuring the view from outside. With all the families gathered in the courtyard, Douglas has just explained the life charts that the orphans are being asked to draw. In his translation, Rodger tried to make it sound as harmless as possible, but some of the keener children know what it boils down to: Dip into the pain, expose it, bring it to the surface again and hope it doesn't ruin a week that was otherwise sublime.

Silas notices the change immediately when he takes the boy's hand to lead him into the room. Flower is behind them, and she sees it, too. His whole body is stiff, his face emotionless. He is not resisting, but he looks more than worried—like he's been asked to do the impossible.

The door clicks shut and the three of them awkwardly take seats around the bed, where Flower sets a few pieces of paper and a pen. She asks Jerry if he understands how to draw a life chart. He doesn't respond, just fidgets and thumbs the sheets of paper. She asks again to no avail.

Silas suddenly remembers his father's way of coaxing him to do something when he felt uncomfortable or scared, and grabs a blank sheet. If it was strange food, Ed would take the first bite. If it was the high dive, Ed would jump first. As Silas sketches a horizontal line across the bottom of the page, he feels an odd emotion rising in his chest. The one thing missing from his childhood was acute, paralyzing pain—he can't remember any whatsoever. There are memories of sadness and broken trust, but nothing catastrophic, like what Jerry must be carrying.

He adds a vertical line with ten hash marks to his graph and pauses, collecting his thoughts. A camping trip at four was the first thing he can remember, so he puts a dot at nine on the happiness scale.

"This is the earliest I can remember," he tells Flower, who inverts the sentence into Mandarin for Jerry. "1989: My family went camping that summer."

Flower tilts her head, which Silas knows to mean she needs help with a phrase or word.

"We went on a trip into the forest, and stayed in a tent," he explains. "We saw wild animals and explored. Boys in America love to camp."

She translates, but Jerry seems to be somewhere else. His blank expression doesn't change, his fidgeting persists and he doesn't look up. Silas is undeterred. Next he draws sevens at ages five and six.

"I can't remember much from those two years, but I'm putting sevens because our home was always happy," he tells Flower.

She nods and gently repeats him in Chinese. No response, no signs of interest from the boy.

And so it goes for several minutes, as Silas graphs a line that never dips below six, and then only because it was the year his dog died. Eights and nines dominate the chart, a fact that does not escape him. He listens to himself describe his large, loving family to a boy who doesn't have one, then recalls his contempt for his parents and their quirks and imperfections. He hangs his head.

His hand slows as he nears the hash mark on the horizontal line that says, "Now." He hesitates, draws a dot at two, then erases it and moves it down to one. Flower sees it and holds her breath; Jerry stops fidgeting for the first time since they sat down. He looks up at Silas, who is staring down at his life chart with a sober expression. The boy says something to Flower, who waits a few moments to pass on the question.

"Jerry wants to know why this year is only a one," she whispers. Flower would have done everything possible to avoid asking; her own curiosity would never have prevailed. But if the boy was finally showing interest, she was not going to discourage it. With no answer from Silas, she meekly points to the last dot and repeats the inquiry.

He sighs, wondering where to start.

"Tell him—" he begins, voice trailing off. "Tell him I was not a very nice person. Back home, I was good at many things, I was popular at college. But I disrespected my parents and drove away many people who loved me."

He pauses for the translation, then continues.

"I grew up happy, with a good family, but I thought those things were not important. I went away to college and worked at a bar, even though it hurt my parents. A couple months before I came here, I was sent to jail."

Flower looks up sharply and halts her translating. She has never met anyone who broke the law seriously enough to wind up in jail.

"I know it sounds bad," Silas adds when he sees her recoil. Jerry tugs on Flower's sleeve and asks what they're talking about.

"He wants to know what you are saying," she says timidly. "Should I tell him?"

"Yes, tell him everything I said. I want him to know."

She complies, and another question comes back from the boy.

"He asks why you went to jail."

"Fighting," he says.

The boy listens and then responds excitedly, punching the air and raising his voice above a whisper for the first time.

"Jerry says he thinks you won," she tells Silas.

"Well, I guess. But then I was arrested, so I kind of lost, too."

The big man's eyes are red, and he is no longer looking at Flower when he speaks.

"It's my family that really lost. My father had to pay to get me out, and my mother was humiliated when her friends saw my torn clothes and the blood on my face.

"But it gets worse," he adds with a faltering voice. "When I went away to college I told them I didn't want to be their son— that I was a new person. And I was. They called me Ace."

He is too lost in regret to notice that Flower doesn't translate the last part. She doesn't need to. Jerry knows by watching Silas that he has done things he wishes he hadn't. The boy knows sadness when he sees it.

So does Flower. Guilt has been her companion for months, whispering into her dreams and souring moments of repose and joy. She knows the shame of a man who has dishonored his family is intense, heavy. Weight—that's what it is. She sees it in Silas. Regret hung around his neck like chains.

The three of them sit for a silent minute before she reaches for Silas' shoulder. He covers his face with a hand and she clears her throat.

"Si-*las*," she says, pronouncing both syllables deliberately, perfectly. She has practiced.

"Silas, I am glad you came to China," she tells him. He looks into her eyes; both have tears on their cheeks. "You are a good man."

He nods, unable to speak. Nothing could feel further from the truth to Silas. Nothing she could have said would be easier for him to reject. But he lets the words soak in, wishing they were even a little true. Hoping someday they will be.

Jerry watches Silas as the big American grapples with a palette of unfamiliar thoughts and feelings. Flower quietly draws a chart of her own. When she speaks, the soft sound of her voice eases Silas back into the moment.

"I was happy child, too," she says, marking sixes and sevens down the white expanse of her life on paper. "My home was in a beautiful village. Small village, but very beautiful—many trees and fields. And my parents are wonderful. The way my father loves children is the only reason I wanted to be a teacher."

At the word teacher, her voice grows wistful, reflective. Silas looks up when she pauses. He says nothing while violent images and noises replay in her mind. Their roles of pained confessor and therapist have been reversed.

"Class was finished," she says distantly, hypnotized by painfully vivid memories. "We shouldn't have been there."

The glaze over her eyes vanishes when Silas coughs gently. She looks flustered, begins to fold her chart. Silas reaches out and firmly grasps both her hands with one of his.

"Keep going," he asks. "Please. It will help."

She agrees to continue and the story of a deadly earthquake unravels from her lips over the next several minutes. Silas is riveted. At points, she switches to Mandarin for Jerry, who is also listening with rapt attention. She manages her memories with poise up to the point when class was dismissed on that awful morning. Over the next several minutes, she finishes the story with just enough detail for Silas to understand.

"This boy," she says, straining to get the words out, "he was like my brother, always following me around the village. He would be the first to greet me when I came home from Beijing, and last to see me go. Now he is dead because of me."

She collapses on the bed, sobbing into the covers, ashamed to expose her feelings to Silas but unable to hold them in. Silas, in turn, is afraid to talk, worried that he might be insensitive or that his cultural ignorance would once again obscure what he desperately wants to tell Flower. Finally, he speaks.

"He is dead because of an earthquake," he begins cautiously. "You were his teacher, and you were teaching. You could not stop the earthquake; you did not know it was going to happen. He just as easily could have died in his own home."

She knows all of this, but comprehension and grief are parallel roads that rarely intersect. Her sobbing continues.

"I can't tell you how sorry I am that your village was destroyed, or that he was killed," Silas says. "But I can tell you that you've made a difference in my life, and even more in Jerry's."

The boy hears his name and perks up; he has been fidgeting quietly on the edge of the mattress. Silas brings a box of tissue from the bathroom and Flower dries her cheeks. She sniffs a few more times, then looks at Silas.

"Difference?"

"Yes, a tremendous difference."

"What it means, tremendous?" she asks.

"It means huge, a lot," Silas answers, waving his hands in the air. "You have reminded me how important children are, and by helping me talk to Jerry, you have made this one of the best weeks of my life. And Jerry," he says, glancing sideways at the boy. "He loves you. I think he will really miss you when he has to leave tomorrow."

She smiles meekly and nods. Neither adult notices when the boy slides a sheet of paper in front of him and draws vertical and horizontal lines.

I draw a one at age six, which is as far back as I care to remember. I wait for Lien-Hua and Silas to finish talking, then pat her on the knee and point to my paper. They look surprised and talk to each other very quickly in English. I have no idea what they're saying, but it seems like they want me to start, so I do. I tell her my story:

"This is the year my mother died," I say. "I was her only child, and I was in the room when she took her last breath. Six years old. It wasn't my father's beatings that killed her, but I still think it was his fault that she died. She was sick, with what I don't know, but I hear her coughing in my dreams sometimes—a deep, howling cough I knew would kill her. I knew it was coming, like when you know it's going to rain."

I pause while Lien-Hua translates for Silas. While she repeats the details about my mother, I do my best to remember her. A woman of fine taste but always poor, she made our home as warm as possible with such a cold man living in it. She would sneak me fresh apples and watermelon whenever she could spare the Yuan to buy them, and she always wanted me to go to school, but father wouldn't let me. One year, during the winter, she spent all week sewing old scraps of material into a blanket for me.

"She was a very kind woman—the kindest I have ever met," I tell Lien-Hua. "And wise. She knew when my father was going to come home in a rage, and would send me to the market. Sometimes I would come home too early, and listen outside the door while he threw her over furniture and into the walls. If he caught me listening, he would slap me and tell me not to eavesdrop. A little spy, that's what he called me.

"A few times I came home from an errand and he was already gone. Those are the worst memories, because I had to search for mother in the dark, find her by her breathing.

Most times she was hiding, but once or twice she was uncon-
scious and I had to get a neighbor's help to put her in bed.

"So that's the kind of man my father was. If he is still a-
live, I'm sure he's found someone else to abuse. But I hope
he's dead."

I gather my thoughts; what else do I want to say about
such painful years? Flower puts a hand on my back as she
translates. She seems sad, seems to think I'm sad. But I'm
not, actually. These are just facts to me, and I really do hope
he's dead. I have since the police station.

I think for a moment before drawing a three at age sev-
en.

"This year was a little better. After mother died, he
seemed regretful, sad at times. But he beat me more often
because there was only me in the house to receive his tem-
per. He even took me to the zoo with tickets he stole from
a scalper. I remember seeing an elephant, a tiger and a really
long snake—but the elephant was my favorite. So big, like
Silas!"

The tall man laughs when Flower translates my comparison. He leans forward on an elbow and messes up my hair.
I'm going to miss that.

Flower says he wants me to keep going, so next I draw a
one.

"I suppose I was really an orphan the day my mother

died, but it wasn't official until I was eight."

I search for a way to begin the story of the warehouse and the police station, the kind officer and the murdered shopkeeper. Flower asks what's wrong and I tell her I'm just trying to remember.

"The day I officially became an orphan, my father took me down to the corner store for cigarettes. He was a chain smoker and it was the only thing he would spend money on. It was a cold day—bitter cold, like I had never felt before—but he made me wait on the curb like always. Only this time he didn't come out. After fifteen or twenty minutes I went inside the store, which was small but packed with food and typical convenience store items. I didn't see my father, so I checked the back room. Then the shopkeeper hit me on the head with a broom handle and I woke up in his car.

"He drove me to a strange part of town, where a man with long hair and three sidekicks were waiting in a nice black car. It had tinted windows, shiny wheels—everything. I locked myself in the shopkeeper's dumpy old ride, but he broke the back window and pulled me out by my hair."

I lift my shirt and point to a pair of long scars where the glass cut me. Silas and Lien-Hua look like they have never heard a good story before; she is translating every thirty seconds or so, and he shakes his head longer each time she tells him more.

"They took me to another part of the city, to an apartment inside an abandoned factory. My hands were tied and
they were working on computers and phones, negotiating
what my price would be, where I would be delivered. But
there was a girl. She saved me—cut the plastic around my
wrists and then pretended to have a seizure while I escaped
into the street.

"Until I saw her, I wasn't sure what the long-haired man
wanted with me. I've met a few more kids in the orphanage
who escaped after years of captivity by men like him. They
were taken to far-away cities and rented out by the night. If
they had taken me, I would have been used for terrible
things—"

I feel the warm pressure of tears in my eyes, but not because of what might have happened to me. I cry for what
must have happened to the girl, and for what some of my
friends have experienced. Not even in my darkest dreams do
I repeat their stories, about who purchased them and what
was done. Had I known then, in that apartment, what I know
now, I would have been too scared to run. I think of the
children who didn't run, of what they must endure—the
nightmares, the scars, the demons that haunt their memories.
They are the hollow children.

Silas and Flower are still leaning forward, waiting to hear
more.

"I ran for about ten blocks until they had almost caught up with me, then hid in an abandoned warehouse. I was in a pile of garbage when I saw the man with the long hair shoot the shopkeeper in the chest. I fell asleep with the dead man staring at me, and in the morning, his body was gone. I could tell they had carried it into the alley and put him in the trunk of a car.

"That morning it was sunny, but cold—there were a few centimeters of fresh snow on the ground, and I was starving. I walked and walked, until my feet went numb, and then I saw a market. As I was biting into a pear I could not possibly pay for, the fruit lady caught me and turned me over the police.

"I was happy to feel the cold handcuffs close on my wrists, to be shoved into the back of the police car, to see the officer with a gun and know that I was finally safe. At the station, the policeman who interviewed me was very kind, but he only asked about my father—why he had left me at the store. He sent a car to my father's apartment. A little while later, a deputy walked in with him in handcuffs, and the officer took me out to see him.

"We walked into the lobby and I yelled, 'Father!' He saw me, but he looked through me, like he recognized his son but no longer felt anything in his heart. The officer asked if I was his and he said that he didn't have a son."

I remember it perfectly, and while Flower translates the last few sentences the scene is resurrected around me—the cuffs slapping against the metal bench, the smell of the station and of my father, the officer's hand on my shoulder, the hot tears running down my cheeks and, later, the long ride to the orphanage. I was alone during that trip, alone in a huge bus for hours as it carried me closer to my fate as a nobody, an unwanted burden. I am lost in the memory, which I have kept hidden since that day. Questions I haven't dared to ask.

Why didn't he claim me?

If even that pathetic snake of a man did not want me, who would?

I have answers, but they hurt so much to consider. I am sobbing, doubled over on the bed. More questions.

What should I have done differently?

Could I have been a better son? Endured his beatings with more honor? Would he have been proud of his son if I was stronger?

The voices in the room sound far away and everything is heavy and dull, even my own body. The room grows darker, distant. Faces losing their glow.

Will I always be unwanted, invisible? Is it my destiny just to endure, to never bring enough joy to another person for them to acknowledge me?

I want to sleep, just to sleep and never come back—not

death, really, because death scares me. But the life that I hear myself describing scares me more. So not life, either. There is so much pain that I feel nothing. I hope for nothing. I am nothing.

In a flash Silas is holding the distraught boy, cradling him on his lap and rocking. Jerry is sobbing, convulsing, oblivious to Silas and Flower and everything but his pain. It is open and stinging all over again, a salted wound, a toxic mixture of memories he had suppressed for three years. Silas feels terrible. He wishes he had never asked Jerry to reach into that past. Now that he knows the story, part of him wishes it could go back to where it was, concealed in the boy's chest, insulated from consciousness by years of distraction and avoidance.

But another part of him—the part that has healed by meeting his own problems this week—hears in the boy's weeping a strangely positive note. He recognizes the first signs of an erosion of bitterness: Honesty, recognition, vulnerability. All things he knows Jerry needs to experience before he can heal. So he tucks the boy's head under his chin and rocks. For as long it takes, Silas will hold him. Until he returns, until love breaks through.

Flower caresses the boy's arm with her fingertips, and the uncontrollable sobbing calms to a gentle, rhythmic sniff. His face is buried in Silas' shirt, his body surrounded by the safety of the man's grip—something he has never felt. It is what eventually brings him back.

Finally, reluctantly, he opens his eyes and sees Silas staring down at him. They look at each other for several long moments; Silas smiles and brushes the tears off Jerry's cheek. Flower murmurs something and the boy nods. She hands him his chart and pencil and he draws a few more dots. A three, a four and a ten. He holds it up for Silas to see.

"The ten, is that this year?" he asks Flower. She nods. "Ask him why it's so high."

She does, and the answer comes back quickly.

"Because he came to camp."

Jerry leans his head against Silas and whispers a few more words.

"He says it's the best week of his life because he met you," she adds. "After all these years, you saw him."

A final word from the boy.

"He calls you *father*," she says, reaching for a better translation. "Only, more lovely. More affectionate."

"Daddy," Silas whispers.

"Yes," she agrees. "He calls you *Daddy*."

Shouting love out the window

The night air is still over the valley, engulfing the slow country road and a hotel full of aching children and subdued volunteers. Silas is standing at the low wall of the balcony, elbows resting on stone, a figure of anger and indignation and grief. Anyone who hadn't known him this week would dare not approach. But one of the other guys, who has just finished drawing life charts with his orphan, walks up next to the broad Kentuckian and stands in silence for several minutes.

"Been following the Big Leagues at all?" he asks eventually.

Silas stirs, rising to his full height and placing his palms on the cool stone.

"I checked a few scores when I was on the Internet yesterday, but the Reds are having a tough season," he answers. "They
lost fourteen to one in Toronto a few weeks ago."

"Where are you from again?"

"Florence, Kentucky—right across the river from Cincinnati."

"Got it," the teenager says softly. They talk low, as if trying
not to wake a roomful of light sleepers. "I'm from Arizona, so I
follow the Diamondbacks. They actually started out the season by
losing two out of three to the Reds, but now they're on top of
their division. Go figure."

"Yeah," Silas snorts, "go figure."

More time passes, more silence punctuated with the chirps of
nocturnal birds and the machine-gun clicking of cicadas. Back
home, both men can talk baseball for hours, but tonight, each
has already forgotten what the other said. Sports, cars and the
rest might as well be on another planet. Tonight, orphans are all
that matter, and the stories they've just heard are embedding
themselves deep in their memories—the type of stories that will
remain in sixty, seventy years, when senility removes the indif-
ferent details of life.

As men do, they find comfort in quiet company, and not another word needs speaking before the younger one bids Silas
goodnight and heads for the stairs.

Silas doesn't mind being alone with his thoughts. They are
dark and tragic, but more importantly, they are authentic. And

in some odd way, they are forming in him a resolve to reach beyond himself after he goes home, to believe again that he can play a part of significance in another person's life—in a word, to *care*.

It has been a week full of life-altering moments, culminating in the half - hour he just spent with Jerry. They both unloaded regret, faced pain. He knows it was therapeutic for Jerry because it was therapeutic for him—he already feels relieved of a great amount of bitterness. If the acid of Jerry's childhood has receded from his spirit in any small way, Silas decides, the entire trip was worth it.

Next he dwells on home for a few minutes. Chasing Mel and appeasing his father were the two reasons he came to China; neither one seems even distantly important now. Somehow, he knows that perspective is the only thing that would truly please his dad.

Ah, Dad. He was known as Ed by his clients at the bank, Eddie by the other deacons at church and members of the home school group. What had they thought when Ed's eldest son, his pride, rejected his advice and values, his affection? Ed was not one to demand total compliance, or even expect his kids to agree with him unconditionally. But Silas had not even bothered to engage. He just walked away.

Silas thinks back to the room, Jerry's story told via translator, and to the boy's last word. *Daddy*. How sublime it was to hear that—but even better to understand what it meant. It meant protection to a boy who'd never felt protected, joy to one whose life had lacked cheer and laughter. Love, when Jerry's only source of it had withered brutally and died years before.

Had Silas ever told his father, in any way, that he valued his protection? His sense of humor? His capacity for deep, meaningful love?

It all boils down to that, he realizes. He also knows they would make cheap words after years of proof to the contrary. It will take actions, not words, to tell his father what he should have already been saying.

At some point, after at least an hour of quiet reflection, Silas is no longer thinking about anything in particular, just letting it all soak in. He does not hear the footsteps behind him, or notice when she sets her hands down by his on the railing.

"Silas," Mel says in her gentlest, most soothing voice. "Who are you?"

He doesn't turn, doesn't move. He has been asking the same question.

"I don't know," he says finally.

"You mean you don't know because you don't want to think about it? Or you don't know because the answer is changing?"

"Probably the latter."

"Do you want to know what I've seen?"

He says nothing, and they both look out over the valley for a moment before she continues.

"I've seen a good-hearted, funny, charming boy consumed

by a selfish, egotistical boy who thinks he is a man."

He grimaces and straightens, ready to leave.

"Wait," she says. "Wait—I'm not finished. I've also seen you become a good-hearted, charming man this week. You were amazing—"

He holds up his hand.

"This," he says, motioning in the general direction of Jerry's room, "this is not about me. This whole week; Jerry and the other kids; life charts—none of it was about me."

She smiles and places her hand on his shoulder.

"That boy adores you."

"Twelve hours," he says, recoiling. "In twelve hours he'll be gone."

"You have no idea how important this week has been to him."

His breath catches. There is a tremble in his voice.

"I wish there was more time."

"You've opened the future to him, and now, for him, there is more time," she answers, lowering her voice to a whisper. "He's felt what it's like to mean something to somebody, what it's like to have a *daddy*."

Silas looks at her and squints to hold in his tears.

"Flower told me," she says. "It's beautiful, Silas. You may not know who you are just yet, but that is a wonderful place to start."

As the humidity of a late Chinese evening swirls around

them, she leans in, tip-toeing, kissing his cheek. His giant form softens and she lays her head against his arm as they talk about Jerry's past—how so much pain could be packed into eleven years, childhood years. They talk about the boy for nearly an hour, laughing and hoping and grieving, until they hear Douglas call for lights out from deep inside the hotel.

"Go to him," she says.

"Jerry?"

"The best memory you could give him is to be there when he wakes up in the morning."

He descends to the first floor and finds Jerry's room in the darkness, twisting the knob as quietly as possible. He lies down at the foot of the bed and drifts asleep to the soft rhythm of the boy's breathing.

The last morning of camp starts out like every other in the lush valley—warm, quiet, sleepy. Neighbors greet each other while they tend gardens and carry laundry toward the river. All around the hotel are signs of a typical Friday dawn.

But inside, dozens of little hearts are about to be torn a-gain—not by sinister fathers or thoughtless tragedy, but pierced, nonetheless. Silas can feel one of them beating when he awak-ens.

He is lying on his left side with his right arm draped over Jerry, who quit his bed at some point in the night to sleep next to Silas. The big man's neck is aching for lack of a pillow; his left

side is numb. But he doesn't move or make a sound. He lies ad-
mirably still until he hears voices in the courtyard. Volunteers
are eating breakfast, Douglas is meeting with his staff.

Silas realizes that Jerry can nap on his way back to the orphanage; if the tables were turned, he wouldn't want to sleep a-
way the last few hours of summer camp. So he lays his hand
lightly on the boy's head, causing him to stir. A few minutes later, they are both awake and hungry. Silas heads into the courtyard to fetch breakfast, and the first person he meets is Mel—
not by coincidence. She has been sitting cross-legged within sight
of Jerry's room since before dawn.

"How'd you sleep?" she asks, winking.

"Sleep?" he says playfully, rubbing his neck and assuming a
limp. "What's that?"

"Did he wake up when you went in?"

"No, but he must have at some point because he was there
this morning, on the floor with me." He puts his arm around
her. "I owe you one."

He returns to the room with several boiled eggs and a variety of dumplings, hoping to find one lacking the mysterious spoon-
ful of ground meat in the middle. He and Jerry eat together,
communicating in their own style of sign language: sharp, quick
gestures and exaggerated facial expressions. As each speaks his
own language, jabbing the air, the other's strange syllables are
music to his ears. They need no translator this morning.

When they finish their eggs and dumplings, Jerry disappears

into the bathroom and emerges with a cupful of cold water. As Silas watches, he takes a sip, but when he turns away again, the boy pours the rest of it down his back and giggles. Silas scoops the boy up and tickles his side, and soon they are wrestling.

At one point, Flower knocks on the door. Hearing nothing but commotion, she enters and is promptly hit with a pillow. An only child, and delicate, she's not sure how to react, but any hope of neutrality is lost when Jerry runs behind her for protection. The fray escalates, and she is in it.

The three of them spend the next fifteen minutes turning the room on its side. Covers are hanging off the wall-mounted air conditioner, a mattress is barring the door to the bathroom, and there are at least three fewer pillows in the room than there had been at breakfast. Everything else is in a heap in the middle of the floor when Douglas walks in.

Hand still on the doorknob and mouth agape, he surveys the disaster like he's not sure whether to laugh or just walk back out again. He finally affixes his gaze on Silas, who is sheepishly grinning on his back. Douglas shakes his head.

"Housekeeping," he says with a straight face.

After a few minutes of small talk, Douglas explains it's time to read goodbye letters in the upstairs conference room. Silas and Flower reluctantly help Jerry pack his things and the three of them head for the stairs. Douglas catches up with them a few yards from the conference room.

"Silas!" he calls impatiently. The big younger man stops and turns with a worried look on his face. Douglas approaches and crosses his arms.

"Nice job this week, mate," he says. "I have to admit, I had my doubts about you—had you figured for a no-hoper. But I was wrong. You loved that lad right, and he won't ever forget it; good onya."

Curtains against the far wall flutter and snap in the breeze. The air in the room and the air outside are approximately the same temperature, but the swirling of it around their shoulders, their faces, is pleasant considering that the heat will multiply throughout the day. Desks clutter the room—desks which were once straight, aligned, a grid embodying orderliness, not unlike life before the living starts. Now there are desks pointing every which way but forward, and a disarray of people in them, confused and exhausted and anxious.

A volunteer is standing between her two orphans, both girls, and their translator is reading a goodbye note in English—it is bittersweet, but mostly sweet. The first girl compliments the American woman's complexion, her kindness, thanks her for "a week of happiness I will never forget."

Others are similar: gratitude mixed with requests—pleas, actually—to reunite next year. A few of the children turn away to hide their tears; a few look like they will be just as content back in the orphanage. But appearances here are as deceiving as anywhere, and as Douglas watches the ceremony unfold, he feels

an ideal balance has been achieved: Show them a good time—
good enough to dread leaving—but provide them with a tool, a
ray, a glimpse, so the going isn't quite as hard once the week is
over. As they feel sad to depart, so should they feel a little better about the future.

About halfway toward the front, on the left side of the
room, Silas sits with his arm around Jerry. Their turn is coming,
and after about a dozen letters they are called to the front. Silas
is dazed, Flower is nervous and Jerry is sniffing gently, having
heard the other letters and realizing how near the end has
drawn. Flower shifts from foot to foot, unfolding the letter the
boy dictated last night.

"Dear Silas," she begins, "when I first came here, I didn't
know what to expect. When I saw you, I was terrified because
you are so big." There are chuckles from the audience, easing
the tension. "You can carry me on your shoulders, even though
I am already eleven years old. And I think you could probably
lift a car, if you needed to."

Silas is not surprised at the letter's opening; his little brothers
still get wide-eyed whenever they see him without a shirt in the
summer. But the next line catches him off guard.

"You are my first true father."

Flower's breath escapes her. She glances sideways at Silas,
who is biting his lip.

"When I went to the orphanage, I thought my life was o-
ver. And it was—for three years, I was a hollow boy. But then

I came here, and met you."

Silas lowers his head and grips Jerry's shoulder.

"I hated my father, but I hate him a little bit less now. I only wish he was more like you. I do not want to go back to the orphanage, but I know I must. I hope I can come again next year. If I do, please meet me here."

Silas nods and props himself up on a nearby desk. He is wiping tears off his face when he feels a little hand in his, squeezing for all it's worth. Jerry is smiling up at him, and Silas collects his thoughts while Flower unfolds his note, which has been translated into Mandarin.

Jerry. My boy.

She reads in Chinese, but Silas knows what it says.

You are so special, so important to me. I came to China for the wrong reasons, but you have given me new love—a new heart to take home. It says Jerry on it.

I know you have been hurt. I know your pain is immense, and it will never fully go away. But I want you to understand that you don't have to let bitterness live inside. You are a smart, healthy boy, and you have a bright future. Look toward that horizon, not the one behind you.

Silas can feel Jerry begin to shake. He looks down and sees the boy's face buried in his side. In one motion, he sits down and pulls Jerry onto his lap.

You taught me this week that love breaks through walls— age, culture, even a different language.

I also learned from you what real love is, and I will never forget. I would travel around the world many more times just to spend five days with you, my boy. You are worth it.

You are worth loving, and I do, Jerry.

I love you.

Yours always,

Silas.

There are a million words that could be said and all either one of them can think about is a heavy hand on a small shoulder getting heavier. A boy getting closer to leaving, closer to no more family again and no more Silas. No more pillow fights. No more pool, no more music, no more love like this: Tight hug a-round a small body. Whispers in a strange language that the boy knows are love. Tears from a big, strong man's eyes that he knows are love. One last smile that is unmistakably love.

The bus is unwelcome as it brings its diesel fumes into the still summer air, and even the usually smug driver is a little soft-eyed this morning. He understands the tragedy of his cargo, knows he's taking orphans back to the status quo. He rolls the bus to a stop, cuts the engine, pulls back on the lever that opens the doors and everyone hesitates. Girls have been crying softly for hours; older boys are cold in their expression, stonewalling that one emotion, pushing it down, holding it at bay until they're a safe mile or two down the road. But Jerry has no such control; poise has not entered his mind and he falls apart. Silas starts a long, difficult goodbye and nearby a translator explains to a boy about Jerry's age that no, he can't go home to America with the middle-aged husband and wife he's been calling Mom and Dad since Wednesday.

Orphans are for orphanages, and back is where they must go—the knowing of which makes nothing easier. Back to the carousel of painful sights and sounds, back to everyday reminders of parents who didn't want them, or died prematurely, or simply looked them in the eyes and shrugged them off. Having known since the beginning that Jerry was a five-day commitment, Silas is yet unprepared to let him go. He squeezes tighter and harder and presses his eyes shut against the bus and its open doors, its empty seats and its gas tank full of enough fuel to put hundreds of miles between him and his boy.

Douglas is dropping hints for the volunteers to put their kids on the bus, to walk them those last ten feet so the driver has them back to the orphanage by lunch. Silas lifts his boy, still gripping him tightly, and Jerry's heaving torso heaves more violently. His tragic sounds are mercifully quiet, a whimper and a sniff, whimper and sniff, but the quietness of it only adds to the urge Silas feels to keep his boy another day, another hour. Another five minutes—anything.

The bus is Jerry's fate, then a long solemn ride home, then the resumption of being an orphan. Held tight in Silas' strong arms, he is not an orphan because an orphan is, more than anything else that can be said of orphans, unnoticed. Unimportant.

Just nobody. And Jerry wasn't just nobody with Silas.

One pace at a time, Silas has subtly moved to the doorstep of the bus. Sucking in a deep breath, he leans forward slowly, so slowly, until Jerry's feet touch the landing. The boy's legs shudder as his weight lands on them and he stands again. Inside, a translator slips her hands around the boy's shoulders and pulls him toward his seat while Silas follows down the outside of the bus.

It came so quickly, this moment. It crept into the valley this morning, stalking each of the children who now sit inside the hot bus awaiting a jolt and first gear toward their orphanage.

Every volunteer is pressed against the side of the bus, sweating and shouting frantic goodbyes. Silas is shoulder-deep in one of the windows, reaching for Jerry's hand. He feels it, clutches it, and looks up at the boy who has melted his bronze shell. They stare at each other for several minutes while Douglas gives the driver directions. Finally, the engine bellows, sending a shudder through the vehicle and renewing a chorus of sobs from inside.

Silas pulls Jerry to the open window and grasps the back of his head. The boy's eyes are bloodshot and weary, but they do not look the same as when he arrived. There is a flicker; the hollowness is gone. Silas kisses his boy on the forehead, leans his cheek against him, and begins to whisper three words repeatedly in story book rhythm.

Silas' boy is crying, but he is also listening, also mouthing the words as Silas whispers them again and again. He curls his tongue to shape an L, touches his lower lip to his two front teeth for a V, and the rest is just vowels. A translator at the front of the bus announces it's time to leave and volunteers start pulling away from the bus. Silas kisses the top of his boy's head and then steps away as the wheels rotate forward.

At the front of the crowd, the big man's chin drops to his chest. He has been relieved of so much this week, cleansed by loving an orphan with nothing worldly to offer, and now that orphan is rolling away into the distance. He feels too weak to watch, too feeble to lift his head and wink one last time at his boy.

Then he hears them. Three familiar words in a familiar little voice. Silas looks up and his boy says the words again, loud and slow, as if they were the only words he has ever wanted to say. And that's what everyone hears as the bus disappears, a little orphan boy shouting love out the window to his substitute father, to a mother who died too early, to a future that does not seem as cruel and hopeless as it once was, and most of all to the idea that there is more than being an orphan, that there is good in the world, even if he does not yet know its name.

In their own words
The true-life basis of *These Three*

I think if I can use the sea water as the ink .
Use the big tree as my pen .
I still cannot write all the love between you and me.

-An orphan's farewell to a Bring Me Hope volunteer

As I sit here in China and write this note, I have tears in my eyes. Like you, I just finished reading the last chapter. And I am overcome, because this fictional story of love and recovery is one I have seen played out over and over in reality. Real children, like Jerry, who believe they are worthless until someone flies halfway around the world to help them see that nothing could be further from the truth. Real volunteers, like Silas, with hearts full of idle love until they meet children who require every ounce of affection they can provide. And real translators, like Flower, who quietly bear their own tragedies as they question the point of life, until they see God's love in action and want it.

When Tom and I talked about the conclusion of this book, we wanted to include some of the real-life backstory upon which the characters and events of *These Three* were based. Much more of what the orphans have told us and experienced at camp is included in Tom's first book, *Love Delivery*. Our wish is that you are inspired to carry on this story—but in China, with a little Jerry at your side, just as hundreds of others have.

I like to say that, if every person spent five days with an orphan, there wouldn't be any more orphanages. Here's why.

David Bolt

David Bolt
Director, Bring Me Hope

'A long way, and much mud'

Charlie was an orphan who spent a week with us in 2006. He told his story to a translator before leaving camp; what follows is that translator's account of the interview.

"When he was 5 years old, his parents divorced. Then his father married again, and took him to live with his stepmother. One day, his stepmother asked him and his father to leave and gave his little sister to them. His father held his hand and walked away from the stepmother's house. 'This was a long way, and much mud,' said Charlie. Then I asked him why they didn't take a bus, and he said to me, 'My dad has no money to buy a ticket.'

"When they were tired, they just took a rest beside the road. They were so hungry, and the sister was crying. His father was angry, but they had no money to buy the food. At the end of the day, his father took them to a small restaurant. After dinner, he had no money to pay, so he gave the little sister to the boss of the restaurant as payment.

"Charlie was sad when he told me that his sister was only two months old. Then I asked him, 'Did you cry?' He said he thought his father was joking, so he didn't cry. When they went away, he realized that his sister had been sold.

"One time, a car hit him, so he can't remember many things that happened before he came to the orphanage. One thing he can remember is that his father took him to live in a hotel, but he still had no money to pay, so he wanted to do the same thing—give Charlie to the hotel boss—but the boss didn't agree. He called the police. The policeman came, caught his father, and took Charlie to his home. Charlie told me the officer took good care of him, bought new clothes for him, gave him delicious food. (Charlie could still remember the good times with the policeman; I think Charlie really has a thankful heart.)

"Then the policeman sent him to the orphanage. He said when he got there, he knew his father went to the prison; he also found himself in the 'PRISON.' The orphanage has high walls and very big gate, and the kids in there can not go outside.

"Charlie is 12 years old, and the normal kids that are his age are usually in grade 6 or grade 7, but he is still in grade 2. That is a sad thing, but he is a smart boy. The last sentence he said from his heart was: 'I want to go out of the orphanage—I want to have a family.'"

'Someone cared for him'

When Sam and Julie Vidler first attended Bring Me Hope camp in 2007, they never imagined the impact it would make in their lives. They quickly found that their medical expertise—both were physicians practicing in Australia—was in high demand in China, particularly where it could assist the poor and unwanted.

Their experience at camp inspired the Vidlers to move to the People's Republic in April 2008 with their two young boys, Thomas and James. The family helped run Bring Me Hope's Nanchang location that summer, then directed a series of orphan camps in the historic city of Xi'an during summer 2009.

As of late 2009, Sam and Julie were in the process of adopting a little Chinese orphan named Maggie, and were working to launch a foster home for children suffering from HIV and Hepatitis—blood-borne maladies that are among the most difficult to treat.

"One of my buddies was a 16-year-old named John," Sam wrote of his early experiences at Bring Me Hope camp. "He was at times awkward, reserved, disobedient, frustrated. Not an easy boy to get alongside and make friends.

"As the week went on, though, he started to soften and even smile. By the end of the week, we were able to do the life charts—for most of his life, his emotions were up and down, but for the last 3 years he had flat-lined. We were able to discuss his future—and refocus his ideas of 'success' away from making a whole lot of money to helping others, and showing Agape love.

"He left that camp with hope—not necessarily concrete plans and definite prospects, but a change of perspective on life, the meaning of fulfillment, the value of considering others, changing his view from looking in to looking up and out.

"He also knew that someone cared for him."

On their blog, the Vidlers explained: "We are a very ordinary family, who have been granted an extraordinary (God-given) opportunity to go to another culture and care for those with the least opportunities, yet with greatest potential."

'Maybe we can't go back forever'

Following Dominic through a makeshift city of government shelters in the summer of 2008, it was hard to imagine how the young Chinese college student found his way to Bring Me Hope camp just two months after a life-altering disaster struck his hometown and displaced his family.

On May 12, 2008, Dominic was away at school in the central Chinese province of Shaanxi when a massive, 8.0-magnitude earthquake surfaced in a picturesque mountain range in a neighboring province. Though he was hundreds of miles removed from the epicenter, he still felt it. As he would quickly learn, that epicenter was within miles of his family's home in the lush mountains of Sichuan. His plans to spend two weeks with Bring Me Hope that summer were the least of his worries.

Dominic's mother was working at her factory job when the earthquake began. During an interview several months later, Dominic said that his mother ran out of the factory when the shaking started, two co-workers at her heels. "But one of her colleagues was not so fortunate," he said. "Her corpse was just about three or four meters from the gate of the factory."

Like many other Sichuan residents who were away from home at the time of the earthquake, it took Dominic several weeks to get back from school to check on his mother. "Communication was very hard—you couldn't get through every time," he recalled.

Official estimates placed the death toll of the Great Sichuan Earthquake at nearly 70,000 people, and at the time of the interview, Dominic wasn't sure if his family would be able to return to their hometown in the mountains, which was still quarantined because of daily aftershocks: "When you're eating, the ground shakes. When you're sleeping, the ground shakes," he said, adding that he had never felt an earthquake before the massive one in 2008 that shook cities as far away as Shanghai, some 1,050 miles east. "Maybe we can't go back forever. The government decided that the area was not safe for living."

Despite the nightmarish events just two months earlier, in mid-July Dominic boarded a train for Zhengzhou, twenty-five hours north by rail, where Bring Me Hope was hosting summer camps. He served as a translator, and said he took special care to teach his assigned orphans about the importance of education. After camp, he rode back to Sichuan and resumed life in the government-run camp for displaced earthquake survivors.

"We are strangers in the shelter, because people were divided into new groups, with new neighbors," he said. "It is crazy that everything should start from zero."

Goodbyes

At night, when I lay awake, I will think of you and my tears will drop. Whatever great difficulties, I will never give up. Trust myself and God. I love you very much and you are important in my heart. My English is not very good. ... Would you like to be my English teacher? I will be your Chinese student and Chinese sister. I miss you—that's all.

– Fiona

The experience I got from this camp makes me feel the love of family. Tracy, our translator, told me you got up very early every day and pray for us. You believe God will bless us. At first I don't believe it. Now I believe God exists.

– Sarah

When I go home, I will miss you every day. By the way, how old are you and why are your eyes blue? And your hair on your arms is really funny.

– Nicole

Though these things are small incidents, I can perceive your endless love. Thank you again for being with me this beautiful week.

– Li Yang

I will study harder in middle school. I am proud of you and you will be proud of me ten years later. You helped me when I was young and I will return to you ten years later.

– Shelly

I heard that you take a very long journey to come here in order to love me. I am greatly moved. Although we only have five days together I feel your love for me. Once, after swimming for a long time, my eyes ached. After you knew it, you remembered the next day and you buy me a pair of diving glasses. My heart is greatly touched. Because you put me in your heart.

– Ivy

Different cultures, different ages, different color skin, different languages—but we can get along with each other. I think this is only because of your love. Thank you. Thank you for the memories you left to me. I will lock it in my deep heart.

– Miah

I'm not an outgoing person, so at first I kept silent, which made you think that I don't like you. However, you know what? In my heart, I can't love you more. I kept silent because I thought the real friends don't need beautiful words to decorate the friendship between each other. A smile is my only way to show our pure and sincere friendship.

When I think about I probably won't see you anymore, I just feel my heart can't beat and I won't have any happy time like now. You give me courage to face difficulties like a family and I hope you won't forget me. Shi Lin in Yun Nan Province—you have a family member there.

– Ja Ja

Jim, I love you! I very love you! Very very love you!

– David